# SURVIVE

*A Memoir*

## SAPPHIRE GEER

ISBN (Paperback): 978-1-7322198-2-3

ISBN (eBook): 978-1-7322198-7-8

Library of Congress Control Number: TXu 2-216-567

Front Cover Artist: Chris Cannon & Clementine Kornder

Book Designer: Lexi Mohney

First Printing Edition 2020

Courage Publishing llc

❀ Created with Vellum

*To all of you who are quietly going through life still trying to make sense of the past. Know that you are stronger, more resilient, more determined, and full of life. That pain you experienced, that hurt, that sorrow does not have to define you and who you are today. We are in control, we choose everything and we choose to live!*

*And to my mother. I love you and thank you for teaching me how to be strong.*

I like living. I have sometimes been wildly, despairingly, acutely miserable, racked with sorrow, but through it all I still know quite certainly that just to be alive is a grand thing.

— **AGATHA CHRISTIE**

I think every kid grows up with their parents' ideals in mind. Even more so if their parents believe girls and boys should be different as they grow. While I was definitely raised with some feminine purposes, like acting like a lady or taking care of the housework, me being a girl never stopped my dad from working us in the name of God and the end of the world.

I questioned many things about my parents' relationship and the reasons they did things that were unique to our family, but I knew better than to voice them.

Having taken the *Book of Revelation* to an extreme view, my whole life was spent moving around North America to live off grid in some of the most remote locations possible.

My childhood was also full of Mom and Dad's honest belief in the end of the world coming for us with the approaching winter. I don't know why they decided

1998 was the year, especially since I'd already been hearing some rumors around church about the millennium coming up, but God's word came through Dad, and Dad told us what we needed to do.

We moved to Grove, Alaska in the mid-90s because we had a family friend willing to loan us their house for a while. It wasn't long before Dad found a cabin in the Yukon that we would camp out in over the summers. Adventuring out in the remote woods was one of my favorite pastimes, so I didn't mind going out there, even if I knew that we were out there preparing for another move.

I couldn't say when exactly the end of the world was coming, but by the way my parents were acting, it seemed like it might be soon.

I STOOD in the tiny hallway outside of our kitchen listening to my parents speak in hushed tones.

Dad's deep grumble drifted through the space, "Cheryl, finished with your seed research, yet?"

I could almost hear my mom pursing her lips in response. "No, Jim. Maybe just a few more plants to research before we're done."

"What the fuck is taking so long? They're just fucking seeds," he snapped, looking for another chance to argue with her. He liked to pick fights when things were out of his control.

She bit back in a harsh whisper, "Do you want to survive and have plants that can handle the conditions or not? If you want it done faster, why don't you just do the research yourself? Or better yet, go out there now without us."

He scoffed, "Lazy bitch."

I held my breath waiting for the other shoe to drop. Luckily, he kept talking.

"You'll do it. I just better have those results in my hands today. The closer we get to winter, the worse leaving is gonna be, and we both know that we are leaving before then."

I could hear footsteps, figuring it was Mom's signature move of shrugging and turning to do something else. It was usually what she did when she was angry but felt there was no point in arguing.

I scowled. I'd been helping Mom do research on those seeds. Dad could even be offensive to me without me being in the room.

The seed project was dumb, in my opinion. Since we had to go to the library to do the research, it became dull and boring. We already had over a dozen plants researched. *How many more do we need?*

I leaned back against the wall looking up at the picture hanging there of a smiling family that was so far from my own in reality. I don't even know why we decided to hang it up since we never decorated with much in the first place.

Having fewer things to pack up made moving easier.

I felt out of place staring at my own smile. Things were definitely happier since we'd gotten to Grove, but they were unraveling in ways that I wasn't ready for. Even if I knew we'd have to leave eventually because that's what *always* ended up happening, I still had hopes that we would just stay for once.

I WAS an oddball in our family. None of us knew who my real father was, but I definitely looked just like him. My hair was long, almost below my waist, and nearly black. My eyes appeared blue or green depending on the light, which were very different from my mom's brown eyes. My face was so round it sometimes reminded me of a porcelain doll. At least, that's what I always thought when I saw my reflection.

Mom and Dad had been planning our next trip for so long, I didn't think we'd ever leave, and in all honesty, I hoped we never would.

*Why can't we be normal for once?* I wondered.

I turned away from the kitchen door, deciding to forego breakfast. If Mom and Dad were arguing about something I was involved in, it was best not to add fuel to the fire.

Slipping down the hall, I almost ran into Paul on my way. He was much taller than me, and I found myself craning my neck to look at him.

As my older brother, I cared for and appreciated him. I could see some resemblance to Mom, but there were also strange features there from some unknown man that made Paul stand out as someone who clearly wasn't one of Dad's children. That he had blond hair, while the rest of us had dark, was a dead giveaway.

Paul had on his usual zip-up jacket and shorts since it seemed his top half was the only part of his body to ever get cold. Maybe it was a nineteen-year-old thing, maybe it was a Paul thing; I couldn't be sure.

He was stocky and broad-shouldered too. I always thought of his movements like those of a lumbering beast, weaving side to side as he walked. I thought it was because he was deaf that he walked the way he did, but no one ever went to get it checked out by a doctor or anything like that.

I waved at him on my way out, but he grabbed my shoulder and turned me around to get my attention.

*"Any news about when we're leaving?"* he signed.

I shook my head in the negative.

He pursed his lips and waved me off along with one of his many odd noises that always reminded me of a sound someone would make if they were telling someone else to screw off.

Being deaf his whole life, Paul was probably the second most coddled of my siblings, and at the same time, maybe the most abandoned. He could make noises, but they were incoherent, and his communication was basic at best.

Considering that he'd been around my whole life, I wished my sign language was as good as his, but neither of us were where we should be since our education consisted of the things our parents thought were important and could teach us. That meant reading, writing, and basic math for me, and an abnormal amount of survival information compared to anyone else my age.

Paul barely had a chance with the lifestyle we led.

. . .

MY CHORES always reminded me of being a farm girl somewhere in the Midwest. Since moving to Grove, Alaska two years ago, when I was nine, I'd gotten even more familiar with taking care of animals.

Feeding time was definitely something I would get into huge trouble for if I skipped out on it. I could spend all day in the woods, but if I wasn't home to give the animals their dinner, I was basically toast.

I knew the neighbor kids, whom we had gotten to know pretty well since moving to Grove, only had to do household things when it came to cleaning, which was lucky for them. Even the boys didn't have to do much more than mow the lawn or sweep the driveway if there were leaves and things.

Since we raised animals, my parents always had me and my siblings do a lot more.

They liked keeping us far away from the hustle and bustle of cities, as well. That meant any news I could get about the outside world, I would devour. It usually came in the form of magazines or catching something on the neighbor's T.V. when I went over to hang out.

The last time I saw anything, it was all about something with President Clinton, but I only caught a second of it. Politics weren't really something we got into in my family, so I was lost on the importance of most of it.

I WALKED over to the pen behind our house to feed the animals and give them some attention. I tossed the corn onto the ground, where all dozen chickens started pecking away at the kernels. Some of the goats started picking off pieces, as well, but one goat, my favorite, came over to me. She knew the secret to getting goodies and treats.

She was brown and white and large for a goat. I'd named her Daisy, and we'd become friends pretty quickly after we'd first gotten her.

Daisy always knew I kept extra treats around for her and some of the other goats. Her baby, Little Milton, was this little black and white goat that looked just like Milton, one of our other goats, and he followed his mother as she came to me. I pulled out some celery sticks and handed them out.

The goats near me were eagerly snatching them out of my hands, and the ones further away quickly made their way over to see what I had for them.

"Calm down! I brought enough for everyone," I told them, holding the celery out of reach of the goats I knew had already gotten a bite.

A sudden gust of wind blew fiercely against my back, sending a deep chill down my spine. It felt ominous, and I didn't like it. I tossed the rest of the carrots and celery into the pen, feeling a need to get back inside before the weather turned. The goats took to a free-for-all, and I scowled, tucking my long dark hair back behind my ears.

"So much for that."

"Sapph, you out here?" Mom called from the back porch. She had on her usual overalls and turtleneck, and her hair fell loose like a curtain down to her waist. She was every bit the woodsy matron and took to the life-style with Dad readily enough.

"Yeah, Mom. What is it?" I asked, turning towards the house.

"Come on inside and help set the table. It's dinnertime."

I left the goats and headed to the back sliding door. We always tried to eat dinner together as a family, so it wasn't an unusual thing to be called in around the same time I fed the animals.

I kicked off my sneakers and began to help Mom set the table and serve the food. In our house, Dad was always served first. It was something Mom felt was important or maybe forced, but no one knew for sure except them.

"Did you wash your hands after playing with those goats, young lady?" Dad asked, scolding me for my poor manners.

I walked over to the kitchen sink and washed up before sitting down at the table, where my brothers and Dad were already waiting for Mom to finish placing the food down.

The Bible said women were subservient, and that was as good as law in our house. It annoyed me that Paul and Andy, my little brother, were just as capable of setting the table, as well, but didn't have to because they were boys.

I would say all my relatives were pretty rugged. We'd spent so much time living in the wilderness or off the grid; it made sense that we adapt and look the part.

My siblings and I could have probably passed in

society with our attire, but Dad looked so much like a mountain man, I would have even believed he was one of those crazy recluse people that head into the woods to plot murder or revenge.

Every pair of Dad's jeans were stained with something. His brown belt, flannel button-down shirt, and big unruly grayish-brown beard were constant pieces of his wardrobe. He had a permanent cigarette stain on his mustache too.

It was hard to explain why, but Dad had the scariest bright blue eyes I'd ever seen on anyone in my life, and a face leathered by the weather and time outdoors.

I remember him shaving his face completely only once in my life, and it was the scariest thing to see even more of his eyes. I was truly grateful when he finally grew his beard back out.

Being scrappy in his youth, Dad had a crooked nose from an unnamed time when he'd likely gotten into a bar fight from assaulting someone.

I could never figure out what Mom saw in him. Better yet, I don't know what Dad saw in a woman who already had a million kids, either.

Still, he was the only dad I'd ever known.

Andy, who was sitting next to Mom so she could help him with his food, was six and exempt from having to do most of the hard labor the rest of us kids did. He was getting to an age where Dad would likely start teaching him the ropes, though.

I couldn't say if our parents would make him because of the massive pedestal they had placed him on since birth, being Dad's only biological child and all. It didn't help that Andy looked just like Dad, either. So, it didn't make sense that the golden boy would be made to do as much manual labor as the twelve of us siblings who were not biologically related to Dad.

While Andy and I were the closest to each other, the way Mom and Dad babied him annoyed me like no other. He liked adventuring and his friends and playing in the woods just as much as I did, but there was no way we could ever do any of that stuff together. If something happened to him on my watch, I think Dad would kill me. It was best just to leave him alone to be a spoiled brat and get in trouble by himself.

As usual, Paul was sitting across the table from me, but he only stared at the food and seemed oblivious to everything and everyone else. He lacked basic manners because no one bothered to teach or correct him, and I was okay with that. Sure it made it hard sometimes, but that was Mom's job, and she really should have done more for him.

My stomach growled, smelling the warm, savory scent of roast beef, potatoes, and carrots, a meal fit for royalty in our house. Usually, it was just beans or rice. It made me wonder what the occasion was that deserved such a feast.

Once Mom sat down, we all bowed our heads, waiting for Dad to start the prayer.

"Heavenly Father, thank you for this meal, and may it provide nourishment for our bodies. Thank you for our family. Thank you for showing us the way and for helping us to prepare for the coming days. We are blessed and humbled by your presence. Amen."

"Amen," we echoed, before we started grabbing our plates and silverware to load up and dig in.

"So, what did everyone do today?" Mom asked. She was in the middle of cutting Andy's food into bite-sized pieces for him.

*What a baby,* I thought, knowing my little brother was definitely old enough to take care of his own food.

I looked up at Paul across the table, but he was busy eating his meal, not paying attention to any of us, and able to get away with it because he couldn't actually hear the question.

The question could only be answered by me, then. I sighed. "I went to the woods for a little exploring."

I watched Mom nod as she finished her cutting and handed the plate back to my little brother.

Dad cleared his throat. "You must have headed out pretty early. We came looking, but we couldn't find you anywhere. Didn't even want to eat breakfast, huh?"

Frowning, I pushed my food around my plate, trying to delay the inevitable. Of course, I'd ducked out when I heard Mom was going to do more of her seed research. Was that so abnormal for an eleven-year-old?

"Sapphire?"

I swallowed. "I wanted to make sure I got more of it in before the winter comes and I'm trapped inside. It's always better to get out there early, and I hadn't seen anyone to talk with about my plans for the day, besides Paul. You know how he is. So, I went on my way and hoped I could ask for forgiveness later if it was an issue."

"You left your mother to do her research all alone

again today, young lady. It's a miracle she even finished it, but I think you owe her an apology. That was half your job, too."

"Sorry, Mom," I said, shoving a bite of food into my mouth so I wouldn't have to speak anymore.

She smiled warmly at me. "It's alright, sweetie. And we have good news! We'll be heading out in two days. Right, Jim?"

I inhaled sharply and started coughing on my food. *Two days?*

Noticing Paul still wasn't paying attention, I swung my right leg and kicked him under the table.

He yelped and scowled at me, signing, *What?*

I stared pointedly at him and then glanced at Dad.

Dad was frowning at me, but continued once he had all of our attention. "Yes, it's true. We are heading to the cabin in a couple days. Bright and early, too, so I expect you all to head up and finish packing what you need once we're finished with dinner."

Paul continued to frown, not quite understanding, or not really believing it if he did. He looked over at Mom, who had a strained smile that made her look tense.

There was worry in her eyes, and she wouldn't look at anyone except Dad.

Paul looked at me for confirmation, and I nodded once. He returned to eating, but he'd started mumbling. It didn't mean anything since he had no way of knowing what words sounded like, but it was a way of letting us know he felt troubled.

I felt for him. I was distressed by the news, too.

I considered my relationship with Paul strained. He was so strange and had so many issues it was hard to feel comfortable around him.

In one instance, I could feel so sorry for him and wish there was better for him, and in others, I would feel irritated because I didn't know how to deal with him.

All the same, he was my brother, and he had it worse than me with his disability, so I usually shoved it all down and dealt with it on my own.

We'd be lucky if this news didn't send him into a fit, though.

WE CONTINUED our meal in silence after Dad's announcement. Even Andy, who was normally chattering away about whatever fun mud puddle or bug he and his friends found, was quiet.

I think it was indicative of how much none of us wanted to leave our lives in Grove. Dad seemed to be the only one on board with the whole thing, and I figure it was more out of pigheaded stubbornness than anything at this point.

No one would be able to talk him out of it.

Paul was the first to get up and leave. He'd rushed eating the rest of his food before rinsing his plate and sticking it in the sink for Mom to wash later. I heard his heavy footfalls walk down the hall and up the stairs to his room.

"Sapphire, you'll help your mother clean up the kitchen, and be quick about it. I need to get the trailer ready for the animals," Dad said, delegating tasks so we would be ready to move with haste as the days passed.

I didn't want to do anything, really, but I didn't have a choice to say otherwise, so I just agreed. It was easier to numb things out, even if it seemed like things were happening with a deeper purpose and urgency than any move we'd made prior to Grove.

As I was doing the dishes and cleaning up the table, I could not help but think of all the times my dad would force us to go along with his crazy schemes.

At least, that's what I thought they were.

The sad thing was—as strange as I knew we were— it felt normal to leave. From the time my mom met him, this was our life.

I was only two when they met, and since then, I have always had the feeling we were being followed and hunted. I felt like we never stayed in one place longer than was necessary.

I remember traveling across North America, going from town to town and church to church because it was the only way to afford gas money. I remember finding ourselves along river banks camping out for days, sometimes months, because we were broke down or out of gas, waiting for the next hand out.

Through all of this, as Dad dragged us around searching for "the chosen place," I felt it was just a blip in my life and never thought much of how we lived.

Now, I could feel that things were changing. In what way? I don't know, but some kind of unknown fear started eating me alive.

## ❧ 2 ❧

The days passed in a blur, and the morning arrived when I woke up to Mom and Dad packing up the rest of our stuff in the trucks to leave. We didn't even have a chance to eat breakfast before my brothers and I were roped into helping them load things up so we could get a move on.

We'd been put in charge of loading bag after bag of whole grain wheat into the old powder-blue Ford. They were so heavy that Paul and I had to carry them together, and our height difference made it awkward as we tried to keep the weight distribution even between us.

The intention of the grain was for our livestock to have something to eat over the winter, while we use some to make bread and things.

Mom was really good at making the most out of such a simple ingredient. I'd seen her do it a million times with a million other things. Our primary food staple was rice and beans, after all, so making things less repetitive and boring day to day was key.

I couldn't begin to guess why wheat grain was the feed of choice for our animals, but I wasn't about to question it. I knew it was better to stay quiet about things more often than not.

Through our summer of research, Mom collected lots of seeds for gardening. Many of them were good for growing in harsh conditions, which would suit all of us just fine once the spring came around. Until then, we had a bunch of fresh produce Mom planned on canning as soon as we got to camp.

After we got the grain loaded, the boxes of seeds were packed on top.

It seemed like there were too many boxes of seeds. Like we could have taken up more space with extra food for the family.

Still, I knew better than to question any of it. It would start a pointless argument and usually end in a beating if I wasn't careful.

Once the Ford was full, Dad had us fill the Dodge next. We put lots of tools and all the household belongings in there.

These were the things we'd need for basic living at the old cabin once we got there: our camping gear, sleeping bags, dishes, survival gear, and anything else Mom and Dad considered survival staples.

Since packing to leave had been our life for as long as I remembered, this all seemed reasonable. It was easier to know where to look for things as we were unpacking later if we kept like things together.

"Alright kids. Let's hook this trailer up. Sapphire, you guide the hitch in," Dad said, delegating the task of getting the animal trailer hooked up to me.

He decided it would be best if it was hooked up to the Dodge, which Mom would be driving. It was home-made from some old plywood that Dad put together to get the goats and birds into the Yukon, and he didn't think it needed to be anything fancy to get the job done.

I watched him back up and gestured to him when he was where he needed to be in order to get the trailer hooked up. I moved into getting the animals in the trailer once it was attached to the truck.

I didn't think about it often, but Dad was probably the handiest guy I knew. Besides building our animal trailer from scratch, he was also the main reason that both of our trucks were still alive.

In fact, the Ford had been in the river near town when we'd arrived in Grove. I'd discovered it when I was on one of my adventures and told my parents about it over dinner. Dad was out the next day deciding if he could pull it out or not, and if it was even worth salvaging.

Turns out, it was.


I CAUGHT a glimpse of our neighbors, who'd come out to watch us pack and say a few words to Mom and Dad. They'd been unsuccessful in preventing us from leaving, but I think everyone was hoping that the snow would begin to fall, and it would keep us from going regardless of how stubborn Dad was being.

All of the neighbor kids hung back near their house, and I wanted so bad to just run over there and plant myself next to them and never leave. The frowns on their faces mirrored what I was feeling, and I imagined I probably looked the same way.

Their dad was the local pastor and had been trying to convince my stubborn father to stick around town since he found out what my parents were planning. Everyone knew what we were doing was dangerous, especially as we got closer to winter, but it didn't matter in the end.

They all sat on their doorsteps or peeked through their blinds as we packed. Normally, they would all be out helping us, but I knew they were trying to delay the inevitable.

I was honestly grateful to them for that. At this point, it was all in God's hands, and by the way the weather was acting, I couldn't believe it hadn't snowed already.

God and I had our moments, good and bad. I couldn't tell if He was really there for me. And if He was, why was He making me leave Grove? My best friends were here, my comfortable home. *Doesn't it matter that I am finally happy?*

As we'd been cutting it closer to winter, I prayed harder for that one huge snowstorm that would keep us in Grove. It was always on the tip of my tongue. *Dear merciful God, please, please, please, let it snow buckets!*

I don't know what it was about leaving Grove that

made me feel so sick, but it lingered and festered and ate at me. It's funny how your appreciation of various weather patterns changes depending on what it is you need to happen.

It's not that I minded snow any other time. Each season seemed to have its benefits. Where summer afforded the ability to go to the river or explore the woods, it also left a lot of outdoor chores for us. The fall was all about harvest, and things quieted down with everyone going back to school. Winter had more indoor things to do, but I knew the animals would still have to be taken care of, so you'd have to spend a bit of time outside in the cold to do that. And spring would bring in a new buzz. We'd start planting the garden and enjoying the new growth and longer days.

Even the almost total dark of winter in Alaska didn't bother me that much. There was usually always something fun happening at our neighbor's.

Now, I watched the cars drive by and ducked my head. It was silly on my part to care about the opinions of anyone else, but I couldn't help thinking everyone passing by probably thought we were totally nuts for packing up and heading out in the fall like we were.

Just based on the supplies we had, I wondered if anyone might think we came from a third world country with all the backwoods gear we were hauling. Like living in comfort was a foreign concept to us.

Honestly, it kind of was. Our house in Grove was the first real house we'd lived in all on our own. Sometimes we'd stay in other people's houses with them, but that didn't last long. It seems Mom and Dad thought we were a burden and would have us moving on sooner rather than later.

The people of Grove were incredibly friendly, and the feeling I had living there was unlike anything I felt before. Although I had no concept of what *home* should feel like, being in this community and having a safe space of my own meant home for me.

Until we'd moved to Grove, I'd never given myself permission to make friends or get attached to any one place or thing. I knew it was rare for us to stay too long anywhere, so there wasn't a point in it.

But now that I had friends, having to let them go was one of the worst things to happen in my life. That was saying a lot considering.

The dreadful feeling that accompanied leaving continued to seep into my bones the more we packed. I desperately did not want to go on this trip, which was saying something since I had a great time at the cabin during our last few visits.

Something about exploring the woods and having adventures in the summer never seemed to get old.

Part of me knew we were there in preparation of a new move, which I so desperately wanted to turn a blind eye to, I ignored most of the things we were doing there in favor of exploration.

Now, all I felt was a deep dread that this trip to the cabin was not going to end well. Kind of like when I dreamed that the neighbor girl fell through the ice on one of the ponds we liked to play in. And the next day she fell through the ice in the exact place I saw it happen in my dream.

I tended to trust my feelings for many reasons like this.

I watched my parents rush around anxiously as they finished loading everything we would need into the trucks, and then had us load up and get ready for the journey.

"Jim," I heard Mom say. "Have you seen the sky? I don't think we're gonna make it before the snow falls."

Dad looked up and shrugged. "We'll be cutting it close, but we'll be fine." He flicked his hand in irritation, dismissing her. Then, he took a final drag from his cigarette and jumped in the front seat of the Ford where both of my brothers were already waiting.

## 3

"**S**apphire, get in the truck," Dad called through the open window, urging me into the Dodge next to Mom.

I took a deep breath. The dread in the pit of my stomach was eating my body away like acid. Everything, our house, the scenery, even the sky felt flat, like a theater backdrop. My play was coming to a close.

Looking at Mom, I noticed her glancing at the heavy clouds above us. The ceiling was coming down fast, and I knew we weren't going to have a good time.

I think deep down, Mom knew it, too.

If only we could convince Dad of that before actually hitting the road.

The family next door stood in their driveway, watching us load up. We already said our goodbyes a million times, but I still couldn't believe I wouldn't see her again. That even if the world probably wasn't going to end the way Dad thought, my world was rapidly coming undone.

*What kind of cruel reality did I live in? Why did this life belong to me?*

The truck rumbled to life, and I watched Dad pull onto the road and out of our neighborhood.

"We could stay and let them go, right?" I hoped, although I knew what the answer would be.

Mom sighed. "I'm sorry, Sapph. We can't be separated from your brothers."

She was right, although I can't deny feeling like we could. That would mean they'd have to come back to Grove eventually and then life would have the potential of getting back to normal.

Anything that kept my life as I thought it should be meant more to me than this trip.

Even though we'd made the drive out to the cabin many times last summer, this time it felt particularly long.

*"The things you complain about always take the longest,"* Mom would say. I wondered if she said this to make us stop complaining.

As expected, the rain fell hard almost as soon as we got out of town and didn't stop falling for three hours. Then it turned to snow.

Mom's hands were clenched tight around the steering wheel, to the point that her knuckles were white and I could hear her forced breaths. She seemed frustrated, and her intense glare directed at the back of the truck bed in front of us made me think she was trying to burn holes through it to puncture the back of my dad's head.

He definitely deserved it.

After three more hours of painfully slow driving in the new snow, I recognized where we were and the turn off for the cabin came into view.

Dad stopped after turning off the main highway, and Mom got out to meet him in front of our truck.

They started arguing.

"Jim, we should go back. Look at this snow! We still have ages before we make it to camp—"

Dad scoffed, interrupting her, "This is nothing. So there's a little snow on the ground? We drive fifty miles more and it'll be a little more snow. The roads haven't been bad. Get in the truck."

"No, Jim, listen. It's too late. We can try again next year," she pleaded.

"I said, get the *fuck* in the *truck*."

At the tone he used, Mom flinched and nodded, but I could see her nostrils flare in anger and agitation. She opened the driver's side and climbed back in, looking at me as if she were trying to convey an apology without actually saying it.

*Can't she stand up to him? Just this once?*

The Ford in front of us started rolling and we followed.

The thing Dad couldn't have taken into account was the difference between snow on asphalt and snow on a dirt two-track. The further we went, the road got muddier and slushier, and I noticed the truck slipping more than once.

We were in the middle of the Yukon wilderness, and things would be freezing soon if they hadn't already.

About thirty minutes into the drive down the dirt

road, Dad stopped his truck. Without enough space to stop safely in the increasingly more dangerous road conditions, Mom and I slid our truck right into the back end of the Ford.

We jerked forward on impact. The feeling of the seat belt cutting into my shoulder, along with Mom's arm thrown across my chest to keep me from flying forward, took some of my breath away.

"Sapph, are you okay?"

I nodded, "Yeah. Are you?"

Mom pursed her lips, watching Dad throw himself out of his truck to yell at her.

She got out too, meeting him at the hood of the truck. The yelling started up again, like it had before we left the highway.

"What the fuck was that, Cheryl? You trying to kill us up here? Why the fuck are you following so close? Why didn't you stop?"

"It's icy out here, Jim. Can't you see that? Things are getting worse by the minute! The animals are probably petrified. You're dragging your family through the mud!" she countered.

He snarled, "Don't you use that tone with me! Look what you've done with your stupidity and negligence! Look, this radiator is cracked. You should pray this works, or we'll be fucked!"

"Are you kidding? We're already there! Ever since we overstayed the summer and headed out during a storm!"

"Hey, don't pretend you don't believe this is impor-tant to the wellbeing of us all! God has foretold of this planet's doom for too long now. We are not going back to risk our lives in that chaos when it comes."

She huffed, "Fine, can we drive this thing, or no?"

"We'll have to find some water for it so it doesn't overheat. I think I saw a creek that could be useful. You still have those empty gallon jugs?"

She nodded; they pulled out several empty plastic jugs and walked to a creek that was out of my line of sight.

I wondered how Paul and Andy were doing. Were they feeling the same way I was about this whole situation? Did they care that we were risking everything to live off the grid this time?

I knew Paul was agitated. It was written all over his face, and his whole demeanor hadn't known peace since Dad announced we were officially leaving.

As for Andy, I couldn't tell if he knew what was going on or what all of this meant. I had no idea if he could sense any danger, or if he felt anything about leaving society behind.

He was young, so I hoped there was still some innocence there. Yet, at the same time, I wanted to shake him into opening his eyes to our twisted reality.

This was not normal!

Soon enough, Mom and Dad came back and filled the radiator so we could continue through the snow and ice to our camp.

The road was terrible. We were bouncing all over the place on the two-track. I could only imagine how much worse it was for the animals in the back, especially since we had to stop every fifteen minutes or so to refill the radiator.

As we continued forward, the snow got deeper and the trucks began to struggle even more. I imagined it would have been easier if the trailer wasn't there, but I couldn't be sure. All I knew was it clearly had been snowing out in the woods for far longer than it'd been snowing in Grove. Mom could see it too.

The real problem was Dad, now, as it always had been. Much like everyone else who tried to stop him from leaving, like the pastor and some of the others in town, the weather wasn't going to stop him.

He saw it as a sign from God, like it was a spurring forward and through adversity, no matter what it might cost him.

After hours of traveling through wilderness and snow, we came to these old ruts in the road that were particularly deep. I knew them from the times we came to visit over the summer.

Then, they were really fun to drive over. Right now, however, these ruts didn't look fun at all, and the thrill I imagined we were about to experience, was of a whole different nature.

"How close are we?" I asked, looking at the road.

"About twenty-five miles, I think."

"Do you think we'll make it?"

Mom frowned at the road, not answering me either way.

We decided to let Dad go first to see how he navigated it so we could duplicate the process. It looked like the ruts lasted for about a mile on this clear stretch, so we waited.

Dad worked his way over the road until he got about halfway through, and then he got stuck. I watched Dad get out and move around the truck, kicking the tires and cursing.

Mom got out and shouted at him, "Need help?"

I couldn't hear his response, but Mom did, and she moved back to our truck to talk to me.

"We're gonna have to go help Dad get the Ford unstuck. Do you have your coat?"

I sighed, slipped on my big, green ski coat, and jumped out of the truck to help.

Dad was still cursing, but he pulled my brothers out of their truck and had us all start digging to free the truck. Each time he thought it was free, he told us to push.

It took about an hour of the five of us digging and pushing before it finally broke free, but the clutch on the Ford smelled burnt and horrible by the time we got through the rutted stretch.

Sweaty and exhausted, I looked back at the Dodge that was waiting for us to come get it and take it through the entire process we'd just suffered through with the Ford. As I stared at the Dodge and the ruts, I felt a slight glimmer of hope. The Dodge seemed to sit higher from the ground than the Ford did. Still, the road looked even worse now that we'd torn it apart.

We all walked back to the Dodge to repeat the process. Again, about halfway through, she got stuck too.

Unlike what I had expected, the high center seemed to work against us as we attempted to dig the truck and trailer out. The animals were in a frenzy from being tossed all over the place on the road, and I felt bad for them. At least I could understand what was going on. They didn't have a clue.

"Alright, guys, let's rest for a minute," Dad called, after being unable to get the truck unstuck for several long minutes.

"Dad, are we ever gonna make it to the cabin?" Andy asked, and Dad ruffled his hair.

"Of course, son. We might have to improvise, though," he said, looking around at our surroundings before looking at the truck again.

We watched him think on it for a minute while we cooled off.

"How about we unhook the trailer and see if we can't pull the Dodge through that way? It's weighing her down otherwise, and we can come back for the animals tomorrow when we have more daylight."

Mom looked at him like he'd just denounced God Himself.

Leaving the animals was a huge risk, that much I knew. What if we couldn't make it back to them tomorrow? Mom did not push the point, though.

I wondered why we couldn't just turn around here.

Taking some feed and water out for the animals to survive overnight, we gave them all we could and prayed.

I reached through the bars of the trailer and rubbed

Daisy's head. "We'll be back for you soon, okay? Keep warm with the others till then."

Daisy barely even acknowledged me now that there was food to be had, but I liked to think my words resonated in there somewhere.

Dad was right, though. As soon as we tried to move without the trailer, the Dodge didn't have any problems in the ruts.

Climbing into the Dodge, with Andy and I being squished on Dad's lap and Paul scrunched up against the windshield, we took off for the Ford to drop off Dad and the boys before following them along. By that point, it was already getting dark.

Coming upon another stretch of deep ruts, Dad didn't even stop to consider how he was going to get through this time. He gunned it, speeding and bouncing along the road. I could only imagine how all of our stuff was being tossed around.

Mom and I watched, holding our breath.

He made it about halfway before he, again, got stuck on the road.

Of course, we all got out to help. The sun had set enough that the only good way to see was by the Dodge's headlights. We dug and pushed and dug some more before everything stopped.

Dad got out of the cab to come over and talk to us. "Well, there's no helping shit now. The clutch is toast on this old girl."

"What are you saying?" Mom asked, holding Andy against her body for warmth.

He sneered at the stuck vehicle. "I'm saying we have

to get in the Dodge and pray we make it around the Ford, and to the cabin."

"We won't all fit in there with the food."

"I fucking know that, Cheryl!" he snapped.

We all flinched except for Paul, who couldn't hear the harshness of Dad's words.

Mom pursed her lips and nodded, moving back to the Dodge to start unloading our food from the cab so we could all fit inside.

"Listen, kids, I promise we'll be back first thing in the morning to get the food, and the animals and everything will be just fine. Mark my words, God doesn't let the truly devoted suffer for long," Dad said, moving in the direction of the Dodge to help Mom unload.

Once the food was moved to the Ford, we all crammed into the Dodge. Dad drove, Mom was in the passenger seat with Andy on her lap, and Paul and I were crunched into the two side seats in the back. The real test, now, would be making it around the Ford.

I held my breath, watching Dad recheck the radiator before jumping in and moving us forward. I felt the tires slip into the ruts a few times, but worse than that, we were cutting it so close with a sloping embankment on one side and the Ford on the other. Moving slower than my slowest walking pace, we crept around the old truck, and I could finally breathe when we cleared it.

I think we all sighed in relief once we were past it.

Dad gunned it once we were through. With the threat of darkness and the snow continuing to fall, we made no further stops.

That wasn't good for the broken radiator, though.

While we prayed the truck would not overheat and get stuck, prayer didn't seem to be enough.

The Dodge overheated and stalled out.

"Fucking, son of a—"

"What do we do now?" Mom asked, covering Andy's ears, although there wasn't much good in it, since he'd already been exposed to Dad's foul mouth his whole life.

Dad growled and cursed under his breath, jumping out of the truck and popping the hood to find it smoking.

If only I could use curse words. There were a few I would have been screaming at him for doing this to us. The backlash from saying anything to him would have been horrendous for me, though.

Dad slammed the hood and jumped back into the Dodge to talk to us. "She's toast. We're gonna have to walk from here."

"Walk? How far—"

"Only two miles, I think. Not so far that we can't make it before it's completely dark. We'll be fine."

Before dark? It was nearly dark already! How long did he think it would take to walk? Did he not remember he had a little boy and a woman with short legs? We were all tired and frustrated and just wanted this to be over. I could see Andy already looked exhausted and Mom looked like she was about to lose it.

I blinked at him, dumbfounded. If we didn't have the Ford and left the Dodge here, we would be absolutely without any way out of this frigid wilderness. Totally stranded.

On top of that, if both trucks were dead, how would we bring the animal trailer here? How would we get our food from the other truck that was stranded over twenty miles away?

Speaking of food, I ate snacks along the way, but I was so caught up in the situation, I barely ate anything all day. I began to realize how hungry I was as my stomach growled.

Andy hung back and watched the whole situation transpire.

I wondered what he thought of this situation in his young mind. Was he scared? He probably did not care much, as he had his hand in the chip bag every time I looked at him.

My anger started to boil up at that point, and I silently directed it at Dad. This was all Dad's fault. Stupid, pig-headed Dad for getting us stuck out here. I couldn't stand him.

Mom pursed her lips and nodded before moving Andy off her lap and grabbing some blankets and some of the bare essentials we could carry into camp. It was only what we'd need to survive for the night, but part of me wished I could carry even a little bit more than that just in case. I knew Mom did not want to cross Dad at this point and just wanted to get this over with. When she pursed her lips and moved on, it was usually a good sign Mom was angry, but resigned to the situation.

I hated it. I hated that she never put her foot down and stood up for us.

Dad continued to promise we'd be back for the rest first thing in the morning as we started walking to the cabin. I didn't know whether to laugh or cry about the whole thing.

I could only pray it was true.

Although praying was something I did often, I struggled with faith in the process. I always had.

So many times I cried and prayed when times got tough, which they often did. And I would always feel like my prayers were never answered.

But when I reflected further on it, I knew deep down, to a certain extent, they had been. I mean, we were still standing here, right? When so many times, one of us, Mom or myself, could be lying dead somewhere, from someone's anger and violence. But we always came through to live another day.

That had to be an answered prayer of some kind, even if I hadn't been directly asking for it.

A dark mass came into view beyond the trees that stood out against the fresh snow. Maybe it was me, but the cabin before us took on the appearance of a slumbering monster in the dim light of the sky. Maybe it was irrational, but I hoped it wouldn't eat us alive.

## ❅ 4 ❅

The void in the pit of my stomach, an intense uneasiness, grew into a consuming mass within me. Dad struggled to open the cabin door due to the accumulation of snow in front of it; all while juggling the armload of supplies he was able to take from the truck.

When he finally did get it open, the musty, rotting earth smell wafted out of the space, and it made my lip curl and my nose wrinkle up in disgust. We'd probably leave smelling like this place by the time spring came.

The smell somehow hadn't seemed so bad when we came during the summer. I couldn't tell if it was because everything was all wet now, or what.

The interior of the cabin was just as I remembered it. All one hundred and fifty square feet of it.

We visited a few times over the summer to get a feel for the space, and it was fun to get away from it all for a couple of weeks at a time. That's what camping was supposed to be. Not a long term thing like it seemed to be in my experience with my family.

At least, long term was not how I wanted camping to be.

It was a single room. Our kitchen included a countertop with drawers that sat near one of the three windows. Below it was a cabinet which stored our dishes. There was a wood stove with a cradle of dry wood next to it, which was left over from the summer.

We were very grateful for this since everything outside was wet and snow-covered.

We had a couple of wooden bunk beds on either side of the room, and a little alcove in the corner where Dad had installed a curtain so we could go back and take sponge baths without worrying about anyone else looking.

The outhouse was avoided unless you actually had to "do business" because it smelled so bad. It was easier to pee out in the trees, and I became a master after a lifetime of living without plumbing.

Full darkness fell over our little camp as the sun fell completely behind the horizon. A blustery cold night arrived, and I couldn't help thinking about Daisy.

*Was she warm? Was she scared? How were all of the other animals doing out there?*

I couldn't be sure what the feelings of goats were, but I hoped she'd cuddle up next to the others for warmth, and they'd all last long enough for us to get them and bring them up to camp.

There were oil lamps which hung around the one-room cabin that we brought in over the summer. Mom lit a few of them while Dad pulled some wood from the cradle and kindled a fire in the wood stove.

We unpacked the few belongings we were able to carry in with us and made our beds with the blankets from the truck. Each of us settled in as the stove began to warm up the room. Thankfully, it was such a small space that it wouldn't take very long.

"Well, now that we're finally here, let's talk about a plan," Dad began, getting all of our attention. "When we're up and around in the morning, we can head out to the Dodge and shovel her out. It'll be easier to get the food and animals with a truck than it will to walk, so it should be fine. Mom and Andy can stay here while Sapphire, me, and Paul go out to take care of things. Since we're the strongest, it'll go pretty quickly, and I know we'll be back by the time dinner rolls around."

I closed my eyes as Dad spoke. The wind howled outside and I knew the snow had to be falling. I hoped it'd stop for our sake more than anything. Every once in a while, the wind would change, and you could hear some of the small icy crystals hitting the windows.

Like a nice summer storm, it was lulling, in its own way.

I can't even remember when I fell asleep, but the trip and the snow knocked me right out. Unluckily, it wasn't without dreams.

No trees, no noticeable plant life, not even a land-mark to be seen. Standing in the middle of a frozen wasteland, I cried out, "Mom? Dad?"

Silence fell over me, deadened by the surrounding snow. Then a sudden gust of wind, carrying a burst of snow, blinded me so I could no longer see the path in front of me.

I stumbled through the storm, yelling and crying for help, but no one ever came. I was all alone and left to die in a place I didn't understand. I curled into a ball and wept. My fingers and toes were frozen, surely frostbitten.

*No one will ever know what has happened to me*, I thought, as I allowed the storm to consume me. The wind was already whipping the snow up to collect in a mound over my body.

I SCRUNCHED up my face and yawned, allowing the dim pre-dawn light from outside to wake me. It must have been ridiculously early, but there weren't any clocks at our camp, so I had no idea what time it was.

Waking up couldn't wait, though. I had to pee.

I slipped on my boots and my oversized green coat; then pulled on the door to open it. It swung open to reveal a massive wall of snow. It was so tall that I was eye to eye with it.

I didn't remember it snowing that heavily, but I remembered the wind.

*Maybe it's just windblown?* I tested it, pushing against it with my hand to see if it would fall down.

It didn't budge.

I closed the door to prevent more warmth from escaping, before turning to Mom and Dad to wake them.

"Dad, Dad, we're snowed in, and I have to pee!"

He scowled, not being much of a morning person. To start the day angry and cursing as he did, I wondered, again, what Mom ever saw in him.

"Fine fucking way to start the day," he grumbled, slipping on his boots and opening the door to the same wall of snow I had.

He pulled a shovel from the corner and started shoveling away the snow enough so I could get out. It wasn't a very big path, but I didn't care at that point. I needed to *go!*

It had snowed almost four feet since yesterday. I couldn't believe it. I don't think any of us could.

As I stepped over it, it packed together, causing me to sink up to my waist with every step.

*This would be perfect for building a snowman,* I thought, wading through the deep rifts until I was far enough away from the cabin to do my business.

I packed down a little spot that was hidden from everyone, but still was enough space for me to do what I needed to do.

As I squatted, I considered the snow around me. There was a wall everywhere I looked.

From my adventurous standpoint, it would be amazing to play in, but I knew I wouldn't be able to enjoy the white wonderland for what it was.

If it snowed this much here, that meant the truck and trailer were probably buried, and we wouldn't be able to drive anywhere.

That thought alone made me feel super uneasy, and I quickly pulled my pants back up and made my way back to the cabin on my already-made trail. It was a lot easier going back than it was trying to get out there.

I arrived at our tiny house to begin the morning. Mom started breakfast: oatmeal with raisins, which she discovered were left behind from a previous trip. I had no idea how any of our food survived with the wild animals that would love a chance to snack on it.

I hated this meal. There was a time in our travels where we were living on the road and all Mom ever made was oatmeal with some kind of fixin'. It was usually raisins because they were easy and could store nicely for a long time. It wasn't that it really tasted bad, but I'd eaten so much of it, that I couldn't stand it anymore.

We sat down to eat as a family and discuss our plan of attack on how to get our supplies and animals. With the amount of snow we'd gotten, we clearly needed to go for a different plan than what Dad came up with last night.

"I figure we can at least head to the Dodge today and see how she fared. We still have supplies in there we can grab, and check to see if the snow is as deep on the road as it is here," Dad said, scooping a bite of food into his mouth. "Since it's a straight stretch, the wind last night may have blown most of it away. If that's the case, the real problem will just be getting out there."

"You think?" Mom asked, already having some doubts. Like mine, they probably never went away, but I think she liked to believe she was giving him the benefit of the doubt.

I couldn't blame her. I was feeling pretty skeptical myself.

"Yes, Cheryl. It happens on other narrow roads. Why would it be so hard to imagine it happening here?"

Mom shrugged, turning away to take another bite.

After breakfast, we dressed in our warmest clothes and made our way out into the snow.

Though it was only two miles away, we spent nearly two hours walking to the Dodge through the snow.

It was a maddeningly slow pace, having to pack down the snow every time we wanted to take a step, and then sinking to our waists. I wondered if this was what it was like to walk through quicksand.

*Maybe it'd be easier to lay on top of it and roll?*

Either way, it was difficult, exhausting work, and by the time we reached the truck, Dad was fuming.

"I cannot fucking believe this shit luck! We're stuck. Fucking stuck! No food. The food we could have is damn near twenty-five miles up the road, probably buried in this white shit that's stranded us, too. Fuck!" he cursed, batting a layer of snow away in his fury.

I sat there in the snow while he ranted and threw his fit. This one was relatively mild, considering many I had seen him throw throughout my life. So long as we stayed out of arm's reach, he usually got it out of his system by beating on the stuff that was frustrating him.

For once, I could understand his anger, and I was also furious with him for getting us into this mess in the first place. He had a million chances to turn around and take us back, but he didn't. I would not devote any sympathy to him in this instance.

The problem was that the essential supplies were carelessly left behind in the Ford. Why did Mom and Dad choose to bring pots and pans, utensils, more blankets, clothes: things we would need only after we fulfilled our basic needs of food and water?

Everything we needed to survive was in the other truck and the trailer. Dad promised we'd be going back to get them today.

That was, until the Dodge got stuck with four feet of snow around it overnight.

Since we were there, we unloaded what was left in the Dodge and walked back to the cabin. With the ready-made path carved through the snow to get out there, the journey back to camp took half the time, and that seemed to brighten our moods to a degree.

It was dark again by the time we made it back. The clouds hung low, darker than they were the day before, threatening another storm. I could pray for it to rain, instead, but I knew it was way too cold for that. Winter arrived a little too late to fulfill my initial prayers for snow.

With this new impending storm on the horizon, the air in our tiny cabin grew thick with tension. The energy between Mom and Dad in particular was rife with anger and blame and worry.

They started to panic, and I wondered if my brothers could tell.

No one said anything as we settled in to weather another snowstorm. We each returned to places we enjoyed over our summer visits. Paul stuck to his top bunk, Andy alternated between Mom's and Dad's laps, and I would tuck myself away in a corner behind the stove. We sat enjoying the warmth of the wood stove and the quiet evening.

To distract us, Dad pulled out a book, *Watchers* by Dean Koontz, and read to us. He did this often when we were moving around, and even more once we settled in Grove.

Despite his choices, and the way he treated Mom, his reading to us was something we all enjoyed. He would read just about any story, from scary Stephen King, to adventurous stories like *Sacajawea* by Anna Lee Waldo, and would even read the Bible from front to back. Of course, *Revelation* was his favorite, and one we happened to hear a lot.

When it came to Dad, his reading was like the calm in the eye of a hurricane. Full of animation and depth. It would take me away. I wanted Reading Dad to be around all the time.

We fell asleep to another night of wind and snow pelting the windows of the cabin. Something I hoped would quiet down before the morning came.

WE WOKE up to even more snow on the ground the next morning, and it continued to fall.

We had to re-carve our paths to use the bathroom, but we didn't want to make the trek out to the truck until it stopped snowing completely.

As the fat, fluffy flakes continued to fall, I gazed out at the forest, feeling like it would never end. My nightmares were coming true, and a weight of hopelessness came crashing over me with each foot of new snow that fell.

I wondered if this was the world actually ending. Like maybe the Bible was right, but not in the fiery doom sense of the end. This one was soft and frigid and biting.

Maybe things were better in Grove. I wondered if my friends missed me as much as I missed them.

My thoughts wandered back to the animals trapped in the trailer, so far away from us without any food or water for the second straight day.

We spent more and more time inside to keep warm and protect ourselves, praying it would be over soon so we could make it out to get some food from the Ford. I think Mom and Dad were giving up on getting the animals faster than I was willing to.

"What are we going to do?" Mom asked, as we came to the end of our second day of being snowed in.

Dad growled, but it was half-hearted. The fear was starting to outweigh the anger within him. "Next time there's a break, we'll just have to head out. There's no other way. Besides, the animals are hardy and will probably live a couple more days. We'll make it by then. We'll just have to hurry when we do."

I pursed my lips, thinking about Daisy. She and the rest of the animals were probably scared out of their minds being cooped up in that small trailer with only each other for warmth.

I could only imagine how they were faring with the wind and snow coming down so intensely last night.

Looking out the window, I watched as even more snow fell against the outside of our cabin.

Never in my life had I seen weather like this. Even in Alaska.

*Maybe it'll never stop,* I thought. *Maybe we'll die.*

## 5

"We have to go," Dad announced to the room after weeks of sitting and waiting out the storm.

I lost count of how many days it had been since we arrived, but we finally came down to our last remaining stored food items; we had no other choice now. The few remaining canned items and a little bit of grain were not going to sustain all five of us for more than a week.

"Who are you taking with you?" Mom asked, holding Andy close.

"Well, if we take the sleds, it should only take us a few days to walk there and return with the food. Sapphire's the strongest, and I think she can handle the journey, so she's coming with me. We'll be able to move through the snow together faster than if I take anyone else."

I pursed my lips, cursing my bad luck. He could have taken Paul out if he wanted to. Paul was also strong, and nineteen. Sure, he couldn't hear, but I was only eleven!

46

Sometimes, I think Dad groomed me specifically to be the one he would choose to help him do dangerous things. Maybe if Paul wasn't deaf, Dad would have been more likely to pick him, but I think Paul's behavior often frustrated Dad.

I think Dad left him alone so he wouldn't get involved if there were arguments either. Since he couldn't hear, he rarely knew what was happening between our parents. But when he did perceive some tension between Mom and Dad, Paul would step in.

He'd get hurt, of course, but Paul could hold his own when needed.

It was easier if I was the only one to step in when fists started flying and Dad started smacking Mom around, though.

There were days I would catch myself wishing I was more like Paul, deaf and oblivious to most of the stuff going on around us. I know it had to be hard on him; he struggled with so much, mentally and emotionally. Some days I wished I had that excuse.

Or Andy, he was happy and ignorant of what was ahead of us. He knew his dad loved him and would do anything for him.

I know Andy saw how Dad treated Mom, and I know it scared him like it did the rest of us, but he never saw the worst of it. Dad always managed to send him off, so he wouldn't witness Dad's violence and try to stop it.

Dad did his best to keep the boys out of it. If anything, Paul was probably the most capable of protecting us, since he was still a strapping young man who'd basically lived and worked off the land his whole life.

But, it would have been bad if Andy tried to stop Dad from hurting us.

I couldn't count the number of times Dad threatened Mom with a gun in her face, and me trying to get in between them to stop it. I know my brothers cared enough that they would have done the same, had they been aware of it.

DAD'S favorite story to tell of my strength and heroism had nothing to do with me getting in the way of him assaulting Mom, but was a time when I was little and we were living near a bull ranch in Montana. I don't remember the details of it at all, but according to him, I'd saved Andy's life from a charging bull.

"From that moment on," he declared, "I knew she was destined for great things. Things that are bigger than all of us!"

That kind of praise was rare in our household, so I clung to it as a shining moment of my life that made my parents, especially Dad, proud. Even if he never treated me like I was "destined for greatness," at least I knew I'd done something right.

AFTER A FEW WEEKS of being stuck out in a trailer with no food or water, we knew the poor animals were probably dead. I couldn't accept it being the truth, even if I knew what living things needed within a certain amount of time to survive. Somehow, I still held out hope Daisy made it and imagined how excited she'd be to see me.

Dad seemed to hold out hope for it, too, as we packed up to head out. He was all about getting out there to make sure there wasn't a possibility of one miracle goat or chicken still being alive after so long.

He had so much faith in God, there was no other option than that in his mind.

I didn't want to be around when that bubble of hope burst and he got angry again.

"Here's some food for your journey. We'll have enough here to sustain ourselves until you get back. Just be safe and get back soon, alright," Mom told us, handing us a bag of canned meat and some fried bread.

On the sleds, we packed one sleeping bag, a tarp, and a magnesium fire starter to help us keep warm each night when we stopped to sleep.

Looking over the spare things we were taking, I felt like we were completely unprepared for this journey, but what did I know? All I knew was we'd come down to true life or death, and I really wanted to make it out of this.

I was willing to do just about anything to see the spring and make it back to Grove and my friends and home. I wanted that for all of us.

Dad pulled me out of bed early, and we set off in hopes of reaching the Ford and animal trailer in a day and being able to come back to the cabin the next.

I wondered if that was feasible, considering how long it always took us to get to the Dodge that was only two miles away, but in many ways, I trusted Dad. Even if he had terrible judgement on many things, I believed he would do anything to get us all through this.

We walked, falling into the snow up to our waists, making very little progress just like before.

I stood back and followed at a slower pace than Dad. The consequences of being within his reach sat at the back of my mind all the time. He'd mutter under his breath when he was angry, and it seemed to be getting worse the further we got into the journey.

By the time midday rolled around, we looked back and could still see the cabin in the distance.

*What a painfully slow journey,* I thought. At the rate we were going, I wondered if we'd even make it there by Christmas.

"Fuck if we're gonna die in this godforsaken place," I heard Dad mumble under his breath, and it was in that moment I felt truly angry with him. I kept thinking about how we could have turned back to Grove a million times, but we didn't because of him.

Stupid, stupid him!

"Sapph, turn around. We're gonna need supplies for a longer journey. We aren't prepared for what this journey is gonna entail," he explained, but I could tell he was frustrated and in one of his moods where he'd like to take it out on something.

I continued to stay out of arm's reach.

The return journey ended up taking half the time because of the path we'd already carved through the snow.

We got back to camp and Mom was shocked to see us.

"What are you doing here?" she asked Dad, who was unpacking some things from our sleds to bring inside.

Dad was still fuming from our failed attempt at making the journey and was itching for a fight all the way back that I'd successfully avoided giving to him. Even if I was furious with him for getting us stranded out in the wilderness in the first place, I knew from experience I was not going to hold up against my father's physical strength.

He threw some of our supplies on the ground and slammed the door so hard the cabin walls shuttered. "Do you think I wanted to fucking come back to this shithole, Cheryl? Do you think I would have dragged us all the way out there and turned around if the fucking God forsaken snow wasn't just as damn impossibly hard to fucking walk through as it was when we had to go to the truck?" He slammed his hand down on the counter and it made a clap that echoed around the small interior of our camp.

I shrunk away into my bunk to avoid being targeted for anything.

Mom took a breath, but I could see her deflating under Dad's immense anger. She didn't dare say a word, just let him rant and hoped for the cleanest outcome.

"I fucking hate this place. We made it as far as the Dodge again and I could tell we weren't going to have any-fucking-thing we'd need to stay out that long. I need to recalculate this, and it's fucking better to do it here than to freeze to death out in this fucking wasteland."

Mom nodded curtly before turning to the grain bag

and scooping some out for what we all knew would be dinner. It'd been our dinner for almost a week now, and I considered adding fried bread to the list of things I didn't really like to eat anymore.

FOR DAYS we waited for Dad to devise a new plan since clearly it was going to be longer than a one day journey.

I was excited to not be spending those nights out in the wilderness, even though I knew with each passing day our situation became graver with our food supply as dangerously low as it was.

"I'VE GOT IT!" he said, as we awoke and cuddled under our blankets during a particularly cold morning.

Mom was building a fire in the wood stove to prepare our breakfast bread while we all remained in our beds, waiting for the cabin to warm up.

"What is it, Jim?" Mom asked.

They weren't arguing much now that we were facing possible starvation. I think they were trying to conserve their energy for more constructive means.

He cleared his throat. "I've decided, I think it'll be best to send Sapphire and Paul out for food. They're the next strongest and they're young, so they'll be able to move faster through the snow than I can."

Mom turned on him. "I'm not sending the kids out there without one of us to help them. That's out of the question."

"Cheryl—"

"No! You are not sending a deaf boy and an eleven-year-old girl out into the middle of nowhere by themselves. That's insane. This whole thing is totally insane, Jim!"

Dad growled as a warning for her interruption but continued, "They'll be just fine. I'll take a few days to train them on how to survive out there. It won't be a big deal. I've even recalculated it, and I think it'll only take them a few days to walk out there and make it back. What's twenty-five miles?"

I wanted to scream at him. I wished Mom would for once in our lives.

*Exactly! So, why don't you walk it and tell us how it is?* I thought, feeling like I was about to trudge into my own snow-covered death.

Mom seemed like she wanted to press the point, but his warning instilled the fear in her that he knew it would. She was no match for him, and they both knew it.

Heck, I knew it from the number of times he'd acted on those warnings with me. Or the times I'd stepped in front of Mom to protect her.

That day, as promised, he started teaching Paul and me how to use the supplies we had to help us survive in the wilderness. He took us out into the woods, not too far from the cabin, and had us practice setting up the tarp under a tree. Dad handed me the magnesium block and taught me how to use it to start a fire, and he had Paul and me collect some tree branches and set them up as a bed we could lay our sleeping bag on to stay dry.

"Alright, kids, I think that'll do it for ya'. But to be

sure it'll work properly, I think you two should have a practice run out here in the elements to be sure you've got the hang of it."

I couldn't say anything to counter him, but I was fuming internally.

*The cabin was right there with my bed and everything, and I had to sleep outside like an animal?* I wondered if life could take me any lower than it already had.

*Really, this is nuts,* I thought, laying in a sleeping bag curled up next to my deaf brother.

It was fairly warm out, which in Yukon winter terms is probably above the negative numbers. *How can anyone think it's a good idea to send two kids out into the wilderness, knowing the eleven-year-old girl is going to be in charge of the venture because the deaf nineteen-year-old is fragile and prone to fits?*

I couldn't even process the insanity of all of it.

"*It'll only be a few days,*" I remembered Dad explaining.

Like that justified any of this in the least.

I heaved a sigh, falling into another fitful sleep where I, again, conjured up a nightmare of dying in the cold, vast unknown where nobody would ever know what happened to me.

By the way things were going, I thought that was a genuine possibility at this point.

## ❧ 6 ❧

I was astounded that Paul and I woke up after our trial night out in the wilderness. Even though it was "warm," I knew there was still a risk. That's why Dad made us take the night to be sure his methods would work in keeping us alive.

We rolled up our sleeping bag and tarp and walked back to the cabin.

Dad was the most pleased about our return, knowing it was him that taught us how to live outside on our own.

"See, Cheryl," he said, "I told you they'd make it. They don't even need me to come along with them anymore. I bet they'll be back in no time!"

Mom seemed a little more peaceful with the idea of sending two of her children out to fetch the necessary supplies for our survival. She only nodded in response to Dad's crowing, not wanting to feed his ego too much, since he was still the reason we were in this mess in the first place.

I couldn't stand any of it. Even though I was scared to go, I was almost grateful to get out and away from Dad. Maybe my ire would be quelled in the wilderness and I could come back with fresh eyes and an ability to tolerate him as a person.

Again, we prepared for the trip to the truck and trailer.

Since we already had almost everything we needed to make the trek, it didn't take us long to finish preparing. Being dangerously low on food and working off rations, there was a sort of silent haste to the way our family went about getting me and Paul ready for the journey.

I'd watch Andy run around the inside of the cabin, play with the few things he had available, or run out to play in the fresh snow, activities I could only dream of enjoying. Sometimes, it made me envy his innocence and lack of responsibility, but then I remembered what we were facing, and I could do nothing but look forward and hope we all could do what we needed to survive this whole ordeal.

Once again, I watched Dad load our sleds with our supplies, including the sleeping bag, fire starter, tarp, a pot to boil snow, and other hand tools we needed to survive a couple of nights in the wilderness.

He assured us it wouldn't end up taking more than three days to get there and back.

Mom made us more fried bread and packed it away with a couple of canteens for water.

The load was shared between the two sleds Paul and I would use to bring everything back when we made it out to the truck. I was grateful the loads were light, and since the sleds were not falling through the snow, it was easy for us to drag them behind us.

It was a welcomed course of action compared to packing everything on our backs. With less weight in our backpacks, we would have an easier time of trudging through the deep snow when the time came.

To give us the energy we'd need for the journey, we spent one final night in the cabin. Not much was said beyond the usual words of assurance and encouragement, but they didn't do much in the way of helping me feel better about the journey as a whole.

I didn't want to admit it to anyone, but I was scared. I didn't want to get stuck out there, or have something happen to one of us and then having to split up so we could get help. Paul was way too fragile to take charge in a situation like that. My mind kept racing with scenarios like Paul being injured and me trying to pull him back to camp, or having to leave him behind with all our supplies to get help.

What would happen to the rest of the family if one of us couldn't contribute?

WE WOKE the next morning to bitter cold.

It was so cold the icy crust that formed on the top of the snow was thick enough that we could walk on it without falling through under our weight, at least a majority of the time.

I considered it a miracle, knowing the trip would be much faster with a flat surface to walk across. I could only hope it maintained the crust so I wouldn't have to worry about carving a path through the snow.

"I figure if that stuff stays crusted over, you two should make it out there in a day, tops," Dad said, voicing my own thoughts.

Mom agreed, "I know you'll still have to spend the night out there, but I pray this holds for you at least most of the way. What a blessing that would be."

I smiled. It was the best news we could part ways with. Only one night in the frozen Yukon wilderness would be a piece of cake. I could sign up for one night. Paul and I already did that the night before last.

I was so excited we could walk on top of the snow, we didn't take the time to consider the downside to how bitterly cold it actually was and what it might do to us as we spent time out there. We bundled up. I wore my green, oversized coat; snow pants; and boots that were too small. Paul wore his normal jeans, black Sorel winter boots, gray hoodie, and a very oversized parka, which I'm sure he found in a dumpster.

All of our clothes were donations that either came to us directly or were things we got from thrift stores or dumpsters. Since I was growing still, most of the things I had were either way too big for me or already too small, and we hadn't taken the time to replace them.

I had hopes of making it back to civilization just so we could replace my boots. I did not like the prospect of spending an entire winter in them when they were already too small.

I swear, Paul only ever seemed to get cold on the top half of his body. He would wear a jacket even in the middle of summer if he could get away with it. My body, however, did not work that way.

As we set out, I was so grateful for the ice crust on the snow. It was so thick it was like walking on pavement. We were making good time, only breaking through occasionally in spots where the ice was thinnest.

I could have done without that part. It reminded us that underneath our reprieve were several feet of frigid heartache and suffering. I didn't want to think about what it would be like to make a path through all of that. I was barely taller than four feet myself.

I decided if it came to it, I'd have to have Paul come in and carve the path, since the snow would only go up to his chest.

It did not take us long at all to reach the Dodge. It was crazy to think we made it in such a short time, but that was the beauty of the ice crusting the snow.

It made me feel hopeful and excited that the miles could feel so short when you're not trudging through feet of snow.

*If this held, maybe we really could make it in a day.* Although, from experience, I knew that it was not likely.

I walked twenty-four miles in a day once, and that was on dry ground. I barely made it in under sixteen hours. So, with these conditions, it was unlikely we wouldn't have to spend at least one night outside. But I was hopeful nonetheless.

Paul also seemed happy and excited with the progress. I'm sure we both were hoping for the same thing: that we would be back in a day or two and every-thing would be fine.

I also think we shared the same sense of urgency to take advantage of the situation. We would look at each other and nod before moving forward.

We didn't stop for a break until we'd been walking for a few hours. The snow completely silenced the world around us, so the only sounds I could hear in the cold, clear, desolate wilderness were the sound of our breathing and the occasional crunch of the snow beneath our feet.

As I sat there, taking in the silence, feeling my heartbeat under my ribs, and wondering what lay beyond the trees, a chill ran through me.

Maybe it was all the adrenaline fueling our journey up to this point, but as soon as we sat down, a para-lyzing fear gripped me, and I realized I was scared out of my mind.

I looked back at the road we'd already traveled and wondered how far we'd come. With the sun high in the sky, it was definitely close to midday. I knew if it came down to it, we could turn around and walk back with enough daylight left.

But then I thought about Dad. He wouldn't take our return lightly, and he'd probably force me into coming back out on this crazy trek with him. Being out here with Paul was way better than being out here with Dad, in my book.

Looking around, the weight of what I was doing, what we were doing, came crashing over me like a powerful ocean wave meant to sweep me out to sea.

The fact that I was hundreds of miles from a real place of warmth and safety crushed me.

A burning in my eyes and nose from tears fighting to fall had me scrunching my eyes shut.

*What am I, an eleven-year-old girl, supposed to do out here?*

How was I going to handle being so far out in the middle of nowhere with my deaf older brother, who might as well have been my younger brother for how useful he'd be in taking care of us? He followed me because that's what he'd been told to do!

Still, I couldn't cry. If I did that, I'd end up scaring Paul and I was not about to start down that road.

There had been times when I'd gotten emotional around Paul and he'd start to panic and freak out. Since handling his own emotions was already difficult for him, taking on other people's emotions was nearly impossible.

One time, I'd broken down and started crying about something, and he'd gotten so upset he started throwing a fit that completely overshadowed mine. I was so shocked I immediately stopped crying and clamped down on everything I'd been feeling and thinking to try and take care of him and calm him down.

From moments like these when I'd been feeling something but someone else started feeling *louder* than me, I learned my stuff was less important than theirs. I had the capacity to hold space and help them through it all, so I did.

Not only that, but I assumed if I started to melt down Paul would see it and immediately turn around to go home. He'd probably throw a huge fit all the way there, too.

None of these outcomes were ideal for me if I wanted to keep us moving.

That left me no other choice, then. I needed to lock my feelings down to give us the chance to keep going.

I lifted my chin, smiled at Paul, and stood up. If I wanted to get this over with, we had to keep moving. I wanted to maximize as many daylight hours as I could to get us through this.

I waved at Paul to follow me and we moved on.

The sun started to rise and the air felt warmer to me.

*What if it gets too warm and the crust melts?* That thought scared me.

*Too much thinking, brain, c'mon,* I thought, as a small panic lodged itself in my throat, making it hard for me to swallow.

After another hour of walking, we came around a bend in the road and the blinding white light reflecting off the snow made my eyes water. The sun was up in full force, and I couldn't do anything but continue forward and power through it.

I heard Paul cry out from looking at the brightness too long. I couldn't blame him for not being able to look away. That was his primary sense and one of the few abilities he had to protect himself; no matter how badly it hurt, he'd rather suffer than go without it.

I wasn't sure how I'd feel in his position. I'd considered him and his deafness often. The way he was treated in our house alone was something I didn't think was right, but I also couldn't figure out what the right way was to go about it.

It made me appreciate what I had, for sure, but I also prayed for him. I hoped he knew I cared for his well-being.

SAs we continued walking over the blinding snow, something started to feel different. With each new step, there was a cracking sound, different from the crunching sound we'd been hearing since we started our journey. Then, suddenly, I broke through the crusted snow up to my knees.

The sharp edges of the surrounding ice that was still intact dug into me painfully. I wondered if we'd taken too long of a break. *Was this how it was going to be the rest of the way? Maybe I should have had us turn back when I was thinking about it.*

All I knew was it was slow-going now that we didn't have a thick crust to walk on.

Worst of all, our legs were scraped every time we fell through. I knew we had to push forward but each step away from the cabin instilled more fear within me.

Desperation slowly seeped in.

As we started falling through the crust at every step, more panic filled my chest and constricted my lungs, as I realized we were going to get stuck out in the middle of nowhere with no idea when we would reach our destination. I couldn't tell how far we'd come. It felt like we'd been walking forever and maybe we'd be there soon, but there was no way to tell, since we had no way of tracking our distance.

Dad had made calculations about our journey, but he probably hadn't factored this into the equation.

Looking back at Paul, I could see that he had a marginally easier time of walking since I'd somewhat carved the path for him.

With having to shield his eyes from the sun and the brightness of the snow, he was practically going by feeling alone.

Since he'd been walking so much slower than me, I stopped to rest and wait for him to catch up. I was sweaty under my clothes from the difficult terrain we'd been walking through and the heat of the sun. My legs were sore from crawling, climbing, and trudging more than I remembered ever moving in one day.

If only I could quit. It seemed I thought about it after almost every step. I wanted it to be so much easier than it was.

That wasn't gonna happen, though.

Paul finally reached me and paused to break for a minute by plopping down into the snow. He signed to me, asking if we were getting close to the truck.

I sighed, signing back that I had no idea.

And that was the truth, I didn't have a clue where we were, how far we'd come, or how close we were to getting there.

Equally exhausted, Paul sat in the snow and rested with me for as long as I would let him. After a short break, we started walking again.

We repeated this pattern many times as the day went on. Walk, sit, rest, repeat. All the while, I felt my anger towards Dad build upon itself in my mind. My thoughts were all I had to keep away the winter silence and the sounds of our breathing.

Finally, I realized the sun was beginning to set and the truck was nowhere in sight. I didn't want to, but we would have to set up camp before it got dark.

Since it wasn't as blindingly bright anymore, it was easier for both of us to see, and I think that made Paul feel a little calmer.

I signed to him, *'We need to make camp for the night.'*

He nodded and threw the lead to his sled on the ground.

I walked off to the side of the road where the tree-line had huge, thick pines, and I looked for a good tree to camp under.

Since I knew it'd be faster if I delegated our tasks, I signed to Paul to start collecting branches to make our bed like Dad taught us two nights back.

I collected firewood so I could make a fire to keep us warm.

Unfortunately, it took way longer than it should since I had only been taught how to use flint to start a fire the other night.

My remaining energy was pretty much zapped by the time I got the fire going.

Paul set up our bed and put up the tarp; and we sat and ate a little while, staring into the flickering flames while darkness settled in around us.

I closed my eyes to the smoke and heaved a sigh. *Dear God,* I thought, *please let us make it through this night. Please keep me and Paul safe out here in the woods and cold. Amen.*

I heard nothing but the silence of the night, the fire crackling with the burning pine, and my own fear-filled thoughts threatening to suffocate me.

After drying our clothes and boots out a little by the fire, Paul and I crawled into our sleeping bag together and allowed the exhaustion from the day to fully take over. I wasn't a light sleeper, but the rustling around of some animal alerted me sometime in the middle of the night.

It sounded small and I didn't feel any fear towards whatever it was, but I clapped my hands to scare it off anyway. It was dead silent after that.

I laid in the dark, thinking and staring at the night sky where the aurora played and danced. The light green and milky white colored my vision, and I allowed the peaceful feeling to lull me back to sleep.

# ❧ 7 ❧

That panicky feeling overcame my body again and I found myself waking up around dawn. I couldn't avoid the fact that Paul and I were miles away from our family and a semi-safe space back at the cabin. We had slept outside for another night in a forest in the middle of winter. This time without the comfort of knowing I could walk a few yards and be safe and warm inside of a building with my family.

It was way earlier than Paul and I were accustomed to waking up, but I could tell my older brother, who was cuddled around me for warmth in our single sleeping bag, was also waking up.

In the silence, with Paul's breath rustling the hairs on the top of my head, I took a moment to pray again. Maybe I was begging at this point, but I didn't care. I would give anything to make it to the stranded Ford with time to spare before the end of our day.

I begged for it with every fiber of my being.

There wasn't much more to do than crawl out of our

warm cocoon and start packing up camp. We groggily pulled on our freezing cold boots, rolled up our bedding and disassembled our little camp.

Since I knew we'd be traveling back this way, I marked the spot of our first camp with a branch in the snow on the side of the road. I intended it to let me know how close we were getting when we made our way back onto the path of least resistance. I didn't think anyone would take it, but I put it near a big tree that would shelter it a little and hopefully prevent it from falling over.

We started walking for what I hoped would be the rest of the journey to the truck. It got cold enough overnight that the snow crusted over just enough to once again hold our weight. I was so overjoyed for the reprieve a few tears escaped me.

That feeling, and the ice, didn't last long, though. The crust was not as hard as it had been the day before, and as the sun came up, it wasn't long before we were falling through as it melted.

I knew winters could be nice, but I had no real experience with such intense sunlight melting what could have been a smooth journey for us. It wasn't like it wasn't still cold enough out, but there was nothing to block the sun's intensity.

There was a moment where I'd considered having us move into the trees to get some shade, but I could tell it'd be a lot harder to walk through there. Since the sun hadn't penetrated the snow through the pine branches, there wasn't a crust to walk on. We would have fallen right through and would have had to swim our way through the snow.

Not to mention, there were plenty of fallen logs and branches and things that were hidden under the white blanket. There was a greater possibility of tripping or rolling our ankles if we tried walking through there instead of on the road.

Instead of desperation and panic, like I'd felt yesterday, today I was just plain angry. I let it bubble up and roil around within me. I didn't care. If I had time to think and stew on it, I might as well let it take its course and fuel me while I was at it.

*How could I be in this situation? Why am I the one that's responsible for this? For our entire family's survival no less?*

Those questions ran through my head a million times, and every time, the answer was always an image in my head of Dad. I hated him.

Part of me wondered if he actually sent Paul and me because he didn't want to go out himself. After that first attempt where it took us ages to even get to the Dodge before we turned back, I was starting to believe that was the case.

And that made me even madder.

A large part of our morning walk was spent with me seething and allowing the anger to roll around inside of me, fueling my forward motion, and me adding up all of the reasons I was justified in being angry. Specifically at Dad.

Again the sky was clear, and the snow was just as bright today as it was yesterday. Absolutely blinding.

As the day progressed, it became more painful to keep my eyes open.

Even the sun seemed to be going against us here. That added fuel to the fire burning within me, too. I couldn't stand it.

When I couldn't bear the feelings anymore, I dropped to the ground in exhaustion. Paul caught up and sat down beside me. He signed to me, mentioning that his eyes were hurting and he couldn't see very well.

*Great. More to add to my plate of ridiculous responsibilities!*

Both of our eyes were already burning and watering. I couldn't be mad at him for a situation we were both in together.

I signed back, '*I know. My eyes hurt, too.*'

I couldn't tell if our shared experience made Paul feel any better.

After a short break, I got us up and kept us moving. I figured the sooner we made it to the Ford, the sooner we could rest and take care of our eyes. Even if my eyes felt like sandpaper after a while, I couldn't stand the thought of us not making it to the truck before the end of the day.

We started using the snow to soothe them. We'd hold snow over one eye so we could see with the other, and then we switched off to give our other eye a break while continuing to walk.

The good feeling never lasted long, which also frustrated me.

Refocusing on something better, I started thinking about Paul. I was so grateful he kept following me. I don't know what I would do if he hadn't. I don't know if he knew what kind of dire situation our family was in.

*Could he really grasp death? Did he understand that if we didn't succeed at this then all of us were going to starve to death?*

Based on the way I was feeling about it, I could only imagine how he was taking it. It broke my heart knowing he was in this position too. I always worried about my family members and what they could tolerate. Paul was so fragile it scared me to think how quickly he could go off in this situation.

It'd taken less for him to go off the handle on other things before. Like the time mom asked me to wash his jacket, and when I went to take it, he freaked out on me, yelling at me in his nonsensical way, pushing me down, and yanking his jacket from me.

I was shocked at that moment before I tried to explain that mom asked me to clean it, and he did not believe me because he did not think his jacket was dirty.

While he was a very smart individual, his comprehension lacked in many ways.

Just a little more fuel to the fire for me.

Unless he was having one of his panic attacks, I found it hard to determine just what he was feeling. Did he actually understand our situation? All I knew was that it wasn't fair for either of us to be out in the cold, trying to rectify a situation Dad put us in.

But Dad put his problems off on us a lot. Our whole life was spent avoiding a situation Dad caused long before he'd ever met our mom.

From the bits and pieces I heard over the years, Dad

was on the run from the law because he harmed someone in their home.

Dad had gotten into it with a person at a bar when he was young, and later that night followed them home, broke in and attacked the person.

Apparently, he'd sobered up and realized his mistake almost immediately and he knew there were consequences that were best avoided.

He didn't want to go to jail, and knowing that court fees would cost money he didn't have, he started running.

While this was just bits and pieces of information I gathered from listening in over the years, I could not put it past him to have done something like that, and based on my parents' pattern of behavior, I knew we were running from something. It was not just his fear, or whatever it was, of the end times.

Though I do believe all of these things combined made Dad who he was, and that was bad for maintaining a normal way of life for my family.

BEFORE I KNEW IT, darkness was taking over the sky. I'd been so focused on keeping us moving in spite of our eyes that I wasn't taking notice. I didn't know how far we'd traveled or how close we were to the truck.

Again, I felt stranded and helpless in our situation. I couldn't stand it.

I forced open my eyes to get a look at our surroundings.

*I think I know that hill,* I thought, catching a glimpse of a slight mound in the growing darkness.

If it was the hill I was thinking of, then the truck would be just beyond it. That would mean we'd made it and could start the trek back tomorrow.

I tapped Paul in my excitement to get him to open his eyes so I could sign to him and tell him the possible good news. I asked him if he felt well enough to push forward just a little bit more so we could see if the truck was beyond the hill.

He signed back, telling me he'd follow me if I wanted to keep going. It was a lot easier to focus without being snow-blinded.

Now that I felt some amount of hope, I couldn't stop. I moved us forward, still at a painfully slow pace, as we continued breaking through the ice crust which the sun had been melting all day.

It felt like forever, but it was probably only thirty minutes before we reached the crest of the hill.

When you're contending with the sunset, I think time acts funny. I'd spent many sunsets feeling the passage of time.

As we crested the hill, I felt my heart sink. The truck was not there. I was wrong.

It took everything I had not to collapse into the snow and cry. I wanted to so desperately, but one look at Paul silenced me.

I'm sure Paul was feeling just as deflated, knowing we could have called it a trip if we'd been there.

And no matter how much I wanted to, I couldn't

make us move any faster. The snow and the sun and everything else was working against us.

I couldn't stand it.

Knowing there was no point in continuing in the dark, Paul and I crawled into the woods, used the last remaining light to build a bed under a tree, and laid down without eating or making a fire.

My eyes were still burning and there was no way to relieve them.

Based on the way Paul kept rubbing at his, I figured he was experiencing the same thing.

I'd heard other kids, even the neighbors, say things about their lives being unfair, especially if their parents wanted them to do something they didn't want to do. But I knew, curled up with my brother in a single sleeping bag, spending our second night alone in the wilderness with potentially serious risk to our lives, that my life was the most unfair of all.

I couldn't be sure, but I probably wasn't the only one who cried myself to sleep that night.

## ❦ 8 ❦

Peeling my eyes open the next morning was met with more difficulty than I'd ever experienced. The crustiness from sleep had somehow been magnified even though I had wiped my tears away so they wouldn't freeze on my face while I slept.

The excruciating pain was nearly unbearable, and even when we cracked our eyes, we were met with blurred shapes and watery vision that forced us to keep them closed.

Being nearly blind, now, the frustration within me built into a monster of a thing. So much anger and hatred: it festered and seethed.

Still, I couldn't act on it.

I literally couldn't do anything about it.

Knowing Paul was worse off than me seemed to quell the beast as much as I needed it to. I wouldn't go on a rampage just yet. I couldn't.

Paul was naturally deaf, had been that way since he

was born, and now that his eyes hurt as much as mine did, he couldn't see either.

That wasn't good.

When I could crack my eyes, I saw him crying and signing to me in frantic, desperate motions. Like he was begging me to end his misery.

If only I could end my own, too. But really, there was nothing I could do. I didn't even know what was wrong with us. There was no way I could fix this.

Unfortunately, he couldn't see me well enough to see I was trying to tell him it'd be okay. We were alive, life was horrible, but we made it through another night. I was more grateful for that than the alternative of freezing to death, even if I wished I could rip my eyes out of my head to ease my pain.

Since there wasn't much else I could do, I grabbed him and held him in a hug. Patting his back in comfort, I imagined what'd happen when we made it to our destination and then got to go back home again. I imagined saving our lives despite this wasteland of a place. I imagined being able to take off my clothes after all these days of freezing and sweating to death, walking and falling through the snow, injuring ourselves, and having to continue.

It wasn't much, but the relief within me was palpable. I think the hug eased Paul a little bit too.

On top of our new lack of sight, we were extremely sore. The intense sunlight reflecting off the snow the day before baked us to a nice crisp, and now, moving around was the last thing I wanted to do.

*Why couldn't we curl back up in the sleeping bag and sleep for a few more days?* I wondered. Lord, I didn't want to do anything but curl up in a ball and cry until things were fixed.

But I couldn't even do that.

When Paul calmed down enough, I started working on getting us ready to go.

I didn't want to, and it took everything I had to get both of us moving and packed up. I had to peel my eyes open about a hundred times to be sure we weren't missing anything.

I tugged on my brother's arm to get him up and moving. We pulled on our frozen boots, an act I loathed now that my toes hadn't had a chance to get warm in days.

It was amazing to think of all the things I'd taken for granted when I had them. Now, here I was in a situation that was forced upon me, and I wondered if this was an instance where beggars couldn't be choosers.

We rolled up our sleeping bag, and with tears in our eyes and no real way to see properly, we started moving down the road, again.

There was a small part of me that knew we couldn't sit and wait out all of the crap happening to us. As much as I wanted to, I couldn't let us be the reason we all starved.

Even if I put every ounce of energy I had into hating Dad and getting us to the truck, I knew I wasn't going to be the reason we all died.

We'd been running low on food before we left camp, and I was scared to death Mom and Andy would die if Paul and I didn't succeed.

Still, I couldn't care less what happened to Dad in that moment. He was the reason we were all suffering.

*Maybe I can convince Mom to leave him,* I thought, pushing through the snow while crawling on my hands and knees and walking when I could.

It was a thought I'd had a few times before. I started thinking about it when we moved to Grove, and I knew there was a risk of losing our safe haven if Dad ever decided to move us again.

While I disagreed with, and was angry about how we lived, I did fear "the government." This included child services, cops, and people who thought differently than us. This was mainly because, while I hated our life-style, I was afraid of being taken from Mom.

I mean, what child wouldn't?

Mom was everything. Even if Dad was there, they were what kept our family going. As much as I wanted us to be more normal, I couldn't fathom life without them and their craziness sometimes.

Since I could remember, I had been coached to not talk to anyone about what we were doing, where we were going, or who we were, though. There were so many secrets that I almost couldn't keep track of them anymore.

I was so tired of it. It was exhausting. I wished I didn't have to live the way we did for so many reasons, but it was all I knew and had to adhere to.

I remember a time we had to cross into Canada, and we had to drop Dad off on some abandoned road where he alone would travel across, and Mom would take the rest of us through the border crossing with the car.

We ended up getting stopped at the border and were told to say nothing. I think Paul was the only one acting normal at that moment since he had no real clue what was happening, but I think my eyes alone revealed my fear of being caught.

I never really understood it, but we were told we'd be taken to some scary place if we ever said anything. I can't even count the number of times we'd get pulled over and the first thing Dad would say was, "Keep your mouths shut, kids. Don't say anything, don't answer his questions. You don't want to be taken away, do you?"

I didn't want us to be separated, so I did as I was told.

It was different now, though. Death was a little too close to home for all of us, and I didn't think any child should have to go through that for the sake of their parent's crazy whims.

Imagining what it'd be like to step out into the world and not have to worry about being hurt by Dad ever again was something I'd dreamt of many times. Being safe in a house with Mom and my brothers, and any of my other siblings who wanted to join us brought me immense joy.

A small smile touched the corners of my mouth.

It was decided, then. That had to be the new goal. And while I was at it, I would work to discard some of Dad's ingrained ideals, as well.

Maybe aiming for a salvation like that would get us to the truck faster. I had to try, at least.

Yet, anger wasn't strong enough to get us very far.

Clearly, or my fury would have gotten us to the truck at least before the end of our second day.

After days out in the wilderness, I couldn't imagine the truck being much further, though. We'd been trudging through the snow at an extremely slow rate, so of course my judge of distance was immensely skewed, but I had to believe we were getting close.

*We had to be, right?*

The morning progressed and the sun rose high in the sky. We had to crawl more than walk as we went, and our journey continued to be excruciating. The whole ordeal was possibly one of the most painful experiences of my entire life. Considering we'd had to farm, fish, hunt, and starve for some of my life already, that was saying something about our trek out to the Ford so far.

With the sun up, the light reflecting off the snow made it impossible for us to see, once again. Just like the day before, we were blinded.

Paul would call out, crying in pain regularly. I think his inability to see was extra traumatizing for him since he used it to navigate the world without hearing. In turn, that made him panic.

Several times we were forced to stop because Paul was frozen in place during a spurt of panicked pain, and there was nothing I could do except grab him and pull him into a hug to calm him down.

The level of emotions within me was becoming far too much to bear, but I knew I had to. If not for Paul, then for the rest of my family.

I had no choice. Strength was absolutely my only option.

It was in these moments of holding him that Paul and I had our greatest trust exercises. He had no idea what was going on, and I couldn't fully communicate with him, either. I had to encourage him to trust me and keep moving. The only way to do that was to reassure him through contact every so often. A pat on the hand or back, a pause to sit down next to each other. Anything to ease the feeling he was alone in this because he wasn't. I was suffering too.

I decided that I had to find a way to keep Paul from experiencing any more pain, and considered what I might use as a blindfold to prevent him from opening his eyes and to keep the light out.

I took my extra pair of socks I brought, thanking the good Lord I had them, and tied them together before tying them around Paul's head. The makeshift blindfold didn't change much since he could barely see even without it, but at least he wouldn't be trying to open his eyes.

It seemed like him forcing his eyes open was most of his cause for panic these past couple of days. Might as well lessen the burden for both of us.

Then, to keep him moving, I took some rope from the sled and tied it to his wrist. *There was one problem solved, at least,* I thought.

I couldn't even say how I was keeping us going in the right direction after that, though. It wasn't like I could see anything either. I kept moving, occasionally forcing my eyes open to get an idea of the blurry objects around us and to be sure we were sticking to the road.

If I wasn't so cold, I could have passed it all off as a dream. For a while, I think I did try to think of it as such. Just one horrible nightmare that was taking up several days of my life. It couldn't have registered as anything else. Nobody else had to experience that kind of fear for as long as we'd been away from the cabin. I couldn't imagine it.

I DIDN'T KNOW how long we'd been walking before I realized we were standing in front of the Ford. It was still daylight from the little I could see when I cracked my eyes, so that was something. But I was so excited to be there; I didn't even care.

We'd made it.

There was a small part of me that couldn't believe it. With all we'd been through, it seemed God finally smiled down on us.

A firework of pure joy exploded in my belly, and I grabbed Paul's hand and placed it onto the truck so he would know we'd made it halfway through our journey.

I barely saw him smile, and I hoped he knew the kind of excitement I was feeling at that moment. I hope he saw the glimmer of hope shining in through the heap of awful we'd been trudging through for the past several days.

We crawled to the side of the truck and scraped the snow away from the door that accumulated there. The truck was practically buried, like the cabin was that first morning I'd opened the door to a wall of snow.

I forced Paul to climb in first before I threw our supplies inside and climbed in myself. I figured I could tie the sleds to the side mirror, and they'd be fine for as long as we needed them to stay out there. Nothing was going to come by and take them.

As I climbed into the cab of the old truck, the feeling of safety within the space was palpable. Nothing could get us in the cab, not even the animals in the wilderness. It wasn't until now, having a metal husk of protection surrounding us, that I even thought about the dangers of wild animals or the discomfort of being outside.

Suddenly, the burden I'd been carrying released a little, and I was feeling emotional. We were still only halfway through our journey. No one at camp knew where we were or whether we'd made it through even one night.

By Dad's calculations, they were probably expecting us to walk through the front door of the cabin today and joyfully bring them food and good tidings.

For the first time, I wondered what they would think when we didn't arrive back at the expected time. I wondered if anyone would try and make their way out to find us.

Part of me hoped one of my parents would come to make sure Paul and I hadn't died out here.

I thought that, if anything, Mom would come to check that nothing happened to two of her babies.

She had to. *She loved us enough to do that, right?*

I figured we'd probably encounter her on our way back at the very least. That thought was reassuring.

I unzipped the sleeping bag and had Paul climb in before I slipped in and snuggled up next to him. Both of us were cold from being outside. Despite that, we were asleep almost instantly.

There was no concern for any other bodily need in that moment. No worries pertaining to our blindness or the time we might be wasting by going to sleep in the middle of the day.

We were exhausted and we'd made it, which was more than enough reason for us to take that time. I let us sleep all the rest of that day and night. Dreamlessly and safe for the first time in days.

## 9

I couldn't say what time it was when I finally gained consciousness again, but as I tried to open my eyes, they wouldn't budge.

They were crusted shut, and they felt like they had glass in them. It was so painful that I started crying, which made it worse since my tears couldn't escape my eyes.

I couldn't see Paul, but I heard him sniffling like he was crying, too. This must have been a million times worse for him. Being deaf already, and now he really couldn't see? My sympathy made me hurt worse for him than I care to admit.

A burning rage boiled up, and I ground my teeth together. *What is with these situations we keep ending up in? Couldn't we get a break anywhere?*

I felt the futility of it all, freezing up what the anger thawed. It wasn't much, but I knew I had to make up my mind at that moment. Things had to change.

*That's it. I am going to get us through this,* I thought,

using the emotions to fuel my drive. We had no other choice now.

Mom and Dad would know something was wrong when we hadn't returned on the third day like Dad calculated, and I wondered if they were able to ration enough food out so they still had things to eat. *Would they be smart enough to make sure they had what they needed until we got back? Would they put blind faith in Dad's plans and rely on Paul and me to get back in time?*

For Mom and Andy's sakes, I hoped they were rationing to eat a bare minimum each day and still saving some for the next.

With Paul starting to panic next to me, I had bigger things to worry about than what we'd end up walking back to when we made it home to our cabin.

I grabbed Paul's hand and squeezed to reassure him we were in this together. If we did not get moving we, and everyone that was in this with us, were going to die.

I knew they were only about twenty-four miles away, yet it might as well have been a thousand with the time it'd taken us to get to the Ford.

I let go of Paul's hand and tried to clear some of the crust from my eyes. It didn't feel like it was working very well, but I couldn't give up. After a while of carefully peeling away at the crust, I was finally able to crack them open enough to see some blurry light and shadow.

It was a horrible idea. It stung to look for more than a few seconds at a time. I could fight through the pain, though. Pain meant I was alive.

I slid out of the sleeping bag and proceeded to get out of the truck. Or try, at least.

When I pushed against the door, something on the outside was resisting me. Apparently, it snowed again while Paul and I were sleeping, and it was enough to prevent me from opening the door.

I rolled down the window and felt the snow fall into the cab and onto my arms. Frowning, I reached out and started feeling around in the empty window space, only to find it snowed enough to cover halfway up the window on the truck.

I growled, realizing I'd have to dig us out.

Putting on my boots and zipping everything up, I wiggled my way out of the cab and into the fresh snow. I made sure I could touch the side of the truck so I could crawl around without opening my eyes, and I made my way to the back to hunt for food.

I wasn't doing anything until I ate something, and I knew some form of food would likely be of comfort to Paul, as well.

As Mom always said, "*You can't conquer the world on an empty stomach.*"

Plus, I knew Paul and I hadn't eaten much of anything in at least 24 hours. Mom's breads she'd packed for us were gone by the second day, as much as I'd tried to make them last.

Digging around the door of the trailer, I was able to pull it open enough to see the supplies inside and reach in. I started pulling things out at random hoping to find something edible.

What was supposed to be fresh produce, as well as

the food in canning jars, were rotted or frozen after sitting out in the elements this long.

Mom had run out of time in getting the produce canned before we left Grove. Maybe it was partly my fault for not helping her more, but I also couldn't understand why the food supplies weren't the top priority going into this.

*And why had Dad been in such a hurry to leave?* I had to believe we'd have more time than that before the world ended, if it was actually going to end.

And so what if it ended while we were still in Grove? That town was so remote I doubt we would even know about the end unless someone came in from out of town to tell us about it.

There was a moment where I felt my heart sink a little thinking about all of the wasted food there, but I couldn't dwell on it for long.

The more I thought about eating, the more I felt my own starvation, so that had to take priority over every other emotion.

I left the trailer and moved to the bed of the truck to see if I couldn't find something there. When I recalled packing, I thought we'd put all of the food things into one truck, so I expected to find other edible things there.

I uncovered bags of whole wheat we were going to use for animal feed and flour. I also found jars of canned meat which Mom had the foresight to make from the pig Dad butchered.

We always managed to have some animals to work with and to raise throughout my life, and while living in

Grove, we were able to keep even more of them than usual because we had the time and the space. In the two years we'd been there, I'd seen llamas, goats, a pig, chickens and waterfowl.

According to Mom and Dad, anything we could use to substitute some of our groceries was a worthwhile investment.

When we left, we were tending about a dozen goats, several chickens we used for eggs, a few geese, which I didn't like because they were always mean, and some ducks.

Even though feeding and taking care of the animals was usually a chore that landed on me, I didn't mind it much. It was better to be outside with the animals than it was to be inside helping Mom cook or clean.

When we had gotten a pig, it proved to be way more work and resources than we could spare as we prepared for the trip into the wilderness.

I had very little experience with pigs. I didn't realize they could be so vicious.

Once Dad and Paul butchered the pig, Mom and I took to canning the meat and storing it to take it out to the Yukon with us.

Since we could milk the goats and get eggs from the birds, they were more useful alive than the pig was.

That was all well and good if my family and I weren't faced with starvation.

*Is this all we have? This can't be everything.*

I frowned at our provisions, going back into the trailer to look again.

Still just the rotten produce.

I racked my brain, thinking about our days of packing. It'd taken so long I couldn't quite remember everything, but still. If this was everything, we were definitely going to starve.

*This can't be everything, though,* I thought. *Why wouldn't Mom and Dad have packed more food?*

It dawned on me a bit too late, but I blame it on the lack of proper sustenance and sleep. All of the vegetables were supposed to last us. Everything could have been stretched if it'd all been canned in time.

My heart dropped. We were doomed.

I grabbed a can of meat on my way back to the cab and crawled back in through the window. Rolling it up, Paul poked his head out from under the sleeping bag and groped around to make sure it was me.

I grabbed his hand and stuck the jar in it so he could feel that I'd brought us some food. That seemed to cheer him a bit, and it brightened my mood substantially.

*Ha, I might be mostly blind, but he's basically Helen Keller,* I thought, letting a giggle escape me.

Whether born of delusion or lack of nourishment, I couldn't say, but I snapped my mouth closed as quickly as the thought passed. *We had to get out of here.*

I grabbed the jar back and struggled to open it. My muscles strained and I felt weak.

*When was the last time we ate? One or two days ago? Forever, at least.*

The lid on the jar popped, and I quickly removed it, excited to dine on my first real food in days. Inside, a crystalized, reddish ice had formed around the meat. It was frozen solid.

I gnashed my teeth, determined to eat, and started feeling around on the dashboard for the glovebox and other spaces that might have something to chip away at the ice with.

The glovebox had a myriad of things, and at the very bottom, I found a butter knife.

*I can always count on Mom and Dad to have some sort of silverware floating around in their cars,* I thought, cracking my eyes open for a peek so I could aim properly.

Hoping for the best, I started stabbing away at the jar. I'd take breaks to see my progress through blurry vision before beginning the process of stabbing away at it again.

Finally, I got to the point where I could pry a small chunk of meat from the ice, and I handed it to Paul. He still couldn't see, so I had to physically stick the meat in his hands, but it made it.

I heard some happy chewing sounds coming from him a moment later, and it reinvigorated my drive to get out a piece of my own.

I started scraping away at the jar for round two, where I would get to eat something. The shaved ice reminded me of a snow cone, but I wasn't about to start licking it. Meat-flavored snow sounded gross no matter how starving I was. But I guess beggars can be choosers in certain situations.

My hand slipped, and the knife struck the inside of the glass jar. There was a cracked glass sound, then the whole rim of the jar shattered into the icy meat and my lap.

*No!*

Tears slipped from my eyes in frustration as I tried to brush the shards of glass away. I was so hungry it didn't even cross my mind that there could be repercussions to stabbing at a frozen glass jar sitting in my lap.

*This was not happening to me!*

I used my bare fingers to feel around on the ice to pick out as many shards as possible. The glass was poking my already cold fingers, and even though I wasn't using my eyes, I was certain there was blood all over the food now.

*God, please make me too cold to bleed, or else be sure I'm not hurting myself too badly,* I prayed, because I was not going to waste any more precious food.

Besides, who knew how long it'd take us to get back and how much we'd be able to carry? We couldn't afford to waste anything.

I resumed chipping away at the ice, and I managed to free another small piece of meat and take a bite. The crunch of glass between my teeth let me know I'd done a horrible job of getting rid of it, but I carefully removed what I could with my tongue before swallowing.

The metallic copper flavor of blood covered my mouth as the meat went down, but that pork was the best-tasting thing I'd ever had in my life after not having eaten in days.

Deciding to throw caution the wind, Paul and I spent several hours in the truck chipping away at the frozen meat for our meal. As we got further into it, more shards of glass would fall off the jar, and we'd have to pick them off. Nevertheless, it was a meal, and one that would last longer and do more good for our bodies than the loaves of flatbread Mom sent us with.

After finishing the jar, I cracked open my eyes to be sure there wasn't anything left. I noticed my hands were a blurry blood-red. Enough that even through the slivers of my eyes, I could see it.

I rolled down the window for a handful of snow to clean them off with before I reached into the glovebox for a napkin I'd passed over earlier.

Having gone through that entire ordeal, I was exhausted. I kicked off my boots again, and I moved into the sleeping bag. I cuddled up next to Paul, who'd been keeping it warm while I worked on our food.

*Dear God,* I prayed, barely able to form another conscious thought, *please give us our vision back tomorrow. Time is so important, and I don't wanna be out here any longer than we have to. I just wanna go home.*

I couldn't say how long I slept, but it wasn't very soundly. Every time I drifted off, I dreamt of my family dying.

## 10

After nearly no sleep at all, I finally decided it was time to get up. My eyes burned, but the little I could see and the amount of light coming in made me think there was still a decent amount of daylight out. I couldn't say how I knew, I didn't have a clue as to what day it was, even, but I knew I would have enough to make it back to the animal trailer.

*God, I wish it wasn't so stinking hard to open my eyes! I wish I could see!*

I scowled. Even if it was horrible, I'd have to work with what I had.

I had to do this.

I thought about Daisy and how many times I'd begged God to keep her alive. I hoped he'd come through for me once in this whole wretched situation. Just once, I wanted something good to happen, for something to go right.

Thoughts of Mom and Andy, even if he was a brat

sometimes, filled my mind, as they had in my night-mares during our rest. I couldn't let them die.

I turned to Paul and noticed him panicking about his complete inability to open his eyelids and see again.

I quickly dismissed the idea of him joining me on my trek to the trailer. I didn't have time to see if I could get his eyelids open.

I grabbed his face in my hands and brushed his shaggy hair to the side. It was the same way Mom would do it to calm him from having a full-blown panic attack, and it worked for the most part.

I pulled the sleeping bag up to his chest after I crawled out of it, and kissed his cheek as he laid down. Now, I could pull my boots on.

Unless I was pulling him along, he wasn't going anywhere. There was some comfort in knowing I had one less responsibility in leaving him with the truck.

Rolling down the window, I grabbed a handful of snow and held it to my eyes to soothe them before grab-bing a bit more to take a bite.

I was so thirsty, I needed it, but I realized what a horrible idea it was as soon as I'd swallowed it. I felt even more parched afterward. That little bit would have to do for now, though.

I pulled myself out of the truck, this time heading down the road to the animal trailer.

I grabbed a sled, and emptied its contents into the truck. I then began the slow walk down what should have been a road, but was a white, expansive snowscape. There was nothing but the treeless areas to guide me on what I thought was the road. I was terrified of what I would find out there.

Since my eyes still hurt so badly, I took to opening them a sliver before walking in the direction I envisioned the trailer was in. Once I had the path set in my mind, I would close my eyes and walk as long as I could stand it, not knowing if I was walking straight into the trees. After going some distance, I would stop to rest, crack my eyes to get the new direction, and do it all over again.

I'm sure anyone who could see my path from above might have thought something was wrong with me. I'd heard drunk people couldn't walk straight either. Maybe they'd think that about me.

Reflecting on everything about my journey, I considered what I was actually walking towards. *What would I find when I reached the trailer? If none of the animals were left, how would we survive the winter?*

*Was I leaving my family to starve because of my failure?*

I shook my head.

God had the answers to this. Did I believe in Him? Yes. Did I understand why He was making me go through this whole thing? No. But I was certain I'd come to find out eventually.

If I knew anything about God, I knew that was just kind of the way He worked. He was mysterious and wouldn't always make sense, but I knew whatever was in store for me was exactly what I needed in order to grow in this life.

There was always a plan, and that offered some amount of comfort in these trying days.

Finally, I rounded a bend in the road and I could see the trailer's blurry outline. I knew I was close if I could see the outline of it against the snow, so I took another short break to give myself everything I'd need to push the rest of the way there.

As I drew nearer, I started listening for the sounds of any bleating from the goats or clucks from the chickens.

The silence that followed made it difficult to swallow. It was then that I knew what I would find, but until I saw it for myself, I continued to hope it was not the case.

Even though I needed to face it, I know I didn't want to at all.

*Please, please, please, God, please!* I begged, before something buried in the snow caught my foot, and I tripped.

I couldn't see it because everything looked blurry and white, so there was no way to tell that there was a mound of anything there.

Wondering what it was that tripped me, I started digging through the snow and dusting it off. A bloated, frozen, dead baby goat laid in the snow next to me.

*Little Milton?*

Chills ran over my body, and I could feel my arms prickle with goosebumps. I looked over at the trailer, horrified to think of what else I would find. Part of me wanted to flee at that moment, but another part of me was curious.

*How did he get out?*

The thought filled my stomach with dread that

nearly paralyzed me right there in the middle of the road. I didn't want to know. I'd been worried about facing the fact that they were all dead, but it seemed much worse to think about them getting out and not making it either.

*Bears hibernate, right?*

That eased my mind a bit.

*Maybe some of them got out and are wandering around the forest. Animals are survivalists, I think. Is it so hard to believe they're out there living happy lives in the wilderness?*

I let my mind continue to bring me some semblance of comfort as I made my way closer to the trailer. Terror was a mild way of describing how horrible I was feeling. I wished I wasn't alone. I wished for a million things as I caught my first whiff of rotting flesh.

The stench nearly made me vomit. If I had anything in my stomach to bring up, I probably would have.

Tears slipped from my eyes as I came to the back of the trailer. I passed a two-foot hole in the side of it as I came around, and I did not want to look inside. I would have given anything not to have to do that ever, let alone in that moment.

The back had another hole in it, and I took the opportunity to hold my eyes shut so I wouldn't have to face any of it just yet. It just so happened that my eyes were overworked by then and I could barely keep them open anyway.

I considered whether or not I'd have the strength to make it back to Paul before dark. I couldn't even guess the amount of time I had left.

*Why is it when you're faced with a bad situation, your*

*brain does everything in its power to make it a little worse?* I could never understand that.

I forced all the bad thoughts back and considered the baby goat in the snow once more.

*What could have been strong enough to make the big holes and drag the goat out?*

I decided I'd put it off long enough and opened my eyes to pull open the doors on the back of the trailer.

*Pepper? Luellen?*

"Daisy!" I cried, seeing my favorite goat in such a horrifying state. I couldn't stop the tears from falling. I'd promised her we'd come back for her.

With that, my greatest fears were realized. The goats and chickens were all dead. Almost all of them were eaten in half and some weren't accounted for at all.

While I'd had childish fantasies of them escaping into the woods, I knew every hope of that had been dashed on the spot.

I figured they were probably buried in the snow like the baby goat, but I wasn't going to search for them.

I was thankful I couldn't see more of it.

I didn't want to know any more, either. It was heartbreaking enough to see what I already had.

There went any chance of us making it through the winter. We didn't have enough food as it was, and without any chickens for eggs and meat, or any goats for milk, I didn't see any way we were going to make it out of this alive.

Besides, winters in the north were dreadfully long. We probably still had another five months or so before everything thawed enough for us to send for help. And with two dead trucks, I wasn't even sure how that could happen.

I wasn't sure how much more I could be broken on this journey. Now, I was torn, feeling terrible for all of our animals' suffering and knowing that was possibly our last lifesaving food source, and it'd been wasted.

Wiping my tears on my sleeves, I sighed. What was done couldn't be undone, so I had to adapt. And with that thought, a new fear gripped me.

With all the dead animals here, having been *eaten*, there must be a predator close by. Even if it wasn't the same one, I imagined the smell probably attracted all kinds of unsavory beasts from the forest.

And there I was, standing by the food source, in no shape to defend myself or run. I had to get out of there.

I left the door open and walked away, praying that if and when I ever had to come back, they would all be gone.

I prayed nature would take care of the horrible mess so I wouldn't have to. I knew if it came down to it, Dad didn't have enough sympathy for things like this to save me from having to do something about it.

Best to just leave it all behind.

As I made the slow trek back to the truck, I cried. It was the first time I'd allowed myself to really feel the emotions that'd been coursing through my system for days. After seeing Daisy like that, I couldn't hold it back any longer.

I cried, feeling angry at my family's situation. I cried in frustration for my limited abilities and resources.

I cried for the poor animals who suffered and died for no good reason.

I thought about more reasons to cry too. My little brother and Mom were relying on me to make it back with food to keep us alive so we could make it through the winter. *What would I do if I got back and they were dead too? How could Paul and I make it through this together?*

*Was I even capable of getting us through more than this?*

As I walked, I worked on kindling my frustration, anger and sadness into a will to survive. That's all I could do, now. Survive this mess and I had a chance of getting away from all of it. I could be a little more normal.

Heck, Dad might even learn his lesson in this and not drag us into another of his crazy schemes to get us off the grid and away from society.

*Ha! Who am I kidding? If anything, it will probably just solidify more of the crazy. Dad can't live without his ideals*, I thought.

But that brought up another question. What was I going to do if Dad started this up again, wanting to move us someplace more remote after we returned to society?

I knew then that I wouldn't be able to take any more of this. It wasn't like I was incapable because all that Paul and I had been through out here proved I was really strong and able. It was more than that. I was emotionally drained. All of the responsibilities I had at that moment made me feel like Atlas as he was forced to hold the world.

It was too much for little ol' me to bear.

*I am only eleven, for Pete's sake!*

I took a deep breath to refocus my energy.

People were relying on me. My family was just as trapped in this hopeless situation as I was.

Paul was waiting for me too. Deaf with eyes sealed shut by eye boogers and crusties. I was sure he was confused and waiting for me, hoping I would be back any second. There was no way for me even to tell him where I'd gone before I left. He had probably assumed I'd gone to get some food and never returned.

I quickened my steps and pushed on.

The trail I made on the way there was deep enough to guide me back with minimal sight. It helped to rest my eyes while still being able to move forward.

They still hurt tremendously, and I could only open them for seconds at a time. The blurry shapes and dark shadows weren't much to go by, either.

It was dark by the time I returned to the truck. I climbed in and took Paul's hand to let him know I was back.

He was so excited that he pulled me into a crushing bear hug that made me laugh despite the situation. I had to encourage him to let me go to remove my boots and climb into the sleeping bag to get warm.

We settled in and slept fitfully for the rest of the night.

## ❧ 11 ❧

The tip of my nose was cold when I awoke cuddled up next to Paul in the morning. Being in the safety of the Ford's cab overnight instead of under the trees and exposed to the elements, allowed us to get some much needed sleep over the past couple of nights. I was more than grateful for the chance to rest.

I tried to blink my eyes, but they'd completely crusted over at that point. Even behind my eyelids it felt like there were shards of glass. It hurt when I attempted to pry them open, but we weren't going to make it far if we couldn't see.

I gingerly touched the surface of my eyelids and was met with a thick crust gluing my eyelashes together. I started picking at it and pulling it away, trying desperately not to rip my eyelashes out in the process.

It felt like ages before I finally cleared away everything that I could feel and tried to open my eyes again.

My eyelashes tore as I pulled my eyelids apart, but

as I opened them, I found I could see more clearly than the day before. Even if it still hurt to hold my eyes open, I was so happy I could see that I didn't mind the pain much.

The light purple hue of the sky told me it'd be another clear, sunny day, but until the sun was up in full force, it'd probably be easier to travel over the snow.

I closed my eyes for a moment to assess the situation as I saw it.

*Okay, Sapph, how many days have we been out here?*

I frowned. *Four or five days?*

I started counting in my head. It was all such a blur that my days had been blending together.

*Five. This is the start of day five.*

Knowing that, I was certain Mom and Dad were probably worried about us. We'd already been gone two more days than we were supposed to be.

I wondered how long it would take before one of our parents came looking for us.

*Mom would probably be the one to volunteer to come looking,* I thought. And if that were the case, I wasn't so sure Mom would make it as far as we had.

Yet, as a child, I hoped Mom and Dad might come for us. I could imagine seeing them coming down the road and my elation in handing this responsibility over to them.

I couldn't sit here daydreaming about this for long. A quick snore from Paul brought me back to reality, and to the harsh truth; I was the one who had to act. Another glance at the sky, proved that it was still early morning. I needed to get up and stop wasting time, but I also needed a plan.

My stomach growled and ached from our days without food, so to begin with, we needed some sort of sustenance.

I wanted to know if Paul could see as well as I could. We'd be able to make better time if I didn't have to do all of the work.

I turned to my brother to wake him and tell him my plan. I gave him a shake, and he started to move. His face was peeling from our sunburns, and his eyes were crusted over in a way that I imagined mine probably had been before I peeled all of the crusties away.

Paul wrapped a vice grip around me when he realized he could not open his eyes at all anymore.

I couldn't sign to him to stay calm, so I did the next best thing. I shook off his grip, grabbed his face, and started gently pulling the crust from his eyes. I cleaned them the best I could while still having to rest my eyes at times during the process.

Finally, when I felt it was enough, I began to pry his eyes open.

He cried out a little as I did so, and I let him go. I gave him a few minutes and tried again.

This time, he realized what I was trying to do and helped me. I was finally relieved when his eyes opened and he looked around for a moment.

I smiled at him, hoping he could see and be reassured that he was okay. That we were going to be okay.

He closed his eyes like he was going to rest them,

but immediately opened them as if he was afraid they'd glue shut again.

I watched him rub them as he kept blinking and staring around. I could tell he could see, and that made me less worried about him and his condition.

Even if we had this victory, I knew it'd still take us some time to heal from whatever happened to us. I wondered if it was possible to get sunburnt on your eyes and if that's what happened to us from the bright reflection of the sunlight off the snow. I wouldn't know for certain until I could ask someone about it.

All I knew for sure is that it was terrifying. Without our eyesight, we would have died out in the wilderness. Now that we were on the mend, I gained a little more hope than I'd had prior.

Since the first part of my plan for the day was complete, I climbed out of the sleeping bag and cranked down the window. It'd snowed again while we slept, so we were back to digging our way out.

With a clearer view of our situation, I could see the truck was nearly buried.

I crawled out of the truck through the open window and made my way to the back of the trailer. I dug through the remaining produce and jars of food there. I frowned at the bulk of it.

There weren't very many jars. Those alone would not get all five of us through the winter, much less a month if we had nothing else.

Of course, the vegetables were all frozen and no good now, so we wouldn't be bringing any of those back with us.

My ire started bubbling up again. *How am I supposed to know what to do next? There is a complete lack of supplies and here I am exhausted, freezing, and in pain!*

I knew no matter which path I chose, it'd never be good enough for Dad. And worse than that, it was not going to get us through the winter.

*What am I going to do?*

As I sat there looking around and wondering if there was anything I might have overlooked, I realized there were bags and bags of animal grain.

They were the very bags of whole wheat, which I had questioned why we were using it for animal feed. This is exactly what we needed right now. Mom would be able to make flour with it.

*I bet if I bring a couple of bags back with some jars of meat, we'd be able to make the food stretch.*

Lord knew the animals weren't going to need it anymore.

I climbed out of the bed of the truck to grab the two sleds we'd left propped up against the front of the Ford.

With only one sleeping bag, a tarp, a camp pan, a cup, and fire starter, I tried to calculate how many bags we could load onto each sled. We wanted as much as possible, but didn't want things falling off. They also needed to be a weight that we were able to pull.

The thought of pulling a lot of weight through the deep snow without proper food and water was another thought that began nagging me.

I went to lift a bag of wheat onto one of the sleds and had to stop to reassess the weight of it. I frowned.

Looking closer, I noticed the fifty-pound weight stamp on the front.

No wonder it was so heavy!

I considered the bags and the sleds again before hefting the first one up and dropping it back down on the sled. I was strong. I could definitely manage it.

That was the whole reason I was sent to get the food, after all.

Paul could also handle some weight. He was a young man; he'd be fine.

I decided to load two bags for each of us. Then I topped one of the sleds off with some jars of meat and figured we could put our gear on top of the other one.

By the time I finished, it'd been a couple of hours. The sky was a little lighter, but based on how early I started my project, it was still fairly early in the day.

I climbed back into the truck when I'd finished. Paul seemed like he could see better now that he'd had time to adjust, which was good. If he could see, that meant he could follow me back to the cabin so we wouldn't have to be out here any longer than necessary.

Knowing he was better gave me one less thing to worry about.

I thought about the trip back and hoped it'd take us less time than the trip out did. Paul and I had already been gone way longer than we were supposed to be, and I knew Mom was probably worried sick by now.

As much as I wanted to sit there and wait for them to come find us, I didn't want Mom out in the elements like that. Andy probably wouldn't fare well either. They couldn't handle it like we could.

I heaved a sigh before waving my hand in front of my brother's face to get his attention. He turned to me, and I signed to him, *Can you see enough to start walking home?*

He nodded, signing back, *I really want to go home.*

I pursed my lips, nodding. I wanted that too.

I did not want to spend a second more than we had to. I was tired and hungry and scared, and I was fed up with feeling all of it. On top of that, I had no idea what our pace would be like having to drag an even bigger load home.

I figured the trail we made coming out would be covered over with the new snowfall we'd gotten over the last two days. This meant we'd have to cut an entirely new trail and take even more time.

Ugh, I was scared. Who wouldn't be? We were facing a strenuous trek back with added weight in the sleds, we were weakened by our lack of food, and we were still recovering from temporary blindness. With all of these thoughts running through my head, I continued to force down the panic. If I let it surface we wouldn't be getting anywhere very fast.

On top of that, I knew we were still recovering from pretty severe sunburns.

Now that I thought about it, I realized Paul and I had hardly gone pee since we'd been out in the wilderness. Maybe once in the whole handful of days.

*Great! Let's tack on dehydration, too.*

We couldn't be back at the cabin soon enough.

The thought of the glass in the frozen meat popped into my head, and I had to stop myself. I'm sure that was a hugely bad idea, but seeing the train of thoughts coming to me, I knew if I didn't manage to suppress them, I'd end up curling up in a ball, and Mom and Dad would have to come get us. And I'd already decided I didn't want to make Mom have to do that. We could either sit around and die like all the poor animals in that decrepit wood trailer, or we would get move on it and head back to the cabin.

I could only hope our raw determination would take us that far.

I was too stubborn to sit around and wait to die.

Making the decision, I signed to Paul to get ready. I wanted to leave as soon as possible, so I told him to be ready in a few minutes.

I wanted to get as far as we could with the daylight we had.

We climbed out of the cold truck and into the colder wilderness. Before we started pulling, I warned Paul that the grain on his sled was heavy. I didn't want him to get upset by our slow pace without warning him first.

He nodded in understanding and grabbed the rope on the loaded sled, pulling it around his waist.

I looked around at the truck and our surroundings, feeling a sudden doubt creep in around my decision. Yet I knew we had to get the food back if we were going to make it. We were all going to die otherwise.

With determination I started walking, expecting Paul to follow for however much time we had left.

## ❧ 1 2 ❧

The sleds were so heavy. It was nearly impossible pulling them through the snow. I couldn't imagine how much more time it'd take us to get back with the weight we had to bear.

Most of the problem lay in the fact that no matter how much we could move, we'd eventually end up falling through the ice crust and lose the momentum we had going. Then the sleds would stop in the middle of their gliding, and we'd have to get them rolling again.

On top of that, the ropes to the sleds were wrapped around our waists, and in order to bear the weight even a little bit, we had to crawl through the snow on our hands and knees.

Instant, horrible, heavy despair sank deep into my bones.

*Why? Why us? Why am I stuck out here in the middle of nowhere with Paul, who is freaking DEAF, struggling to stay alive with this crazy responsibility of keeping all of the rest of my family alive, as well?*

I stewed. *How could I have let this happen to me?*

I looked back at Paul, and I could already see the dried tear tracks on his face. I was sure his eyes were as sore as mine were. They were red and angry and filled with more tears that threatened to spill over.

I grimaced and took a deep breath to calm myself. If he was feeling down, I couldn't have a meltdown. There was no way we'd both make it out if neither of us could keep our train moving.

I waved to catch his attention and motioned for him to keep moving. We were going to be okay, and I told him as much. I wasn't going to let us stop until bedtime.

We crawled on through the snow forever. It must have been hours, but I had no way of keeping track of exactly how long we'd been making our way back.

The weather was a constant gray and windy with snow flurries drifting around us and hitting our faces. I took a moment to be a little grateful we were no longer being blinded by the intense sun, but I didn't think any of it was very good for my eyes.

I was so preoccupied with keeping us on the trail, I hadn't realized my own bodily needs.

I was *thirsty*.

I looked back at Paul and signed to him, asking for our canteen.

He shook his head and signed, *It's all gone.*

I stared at him.

*How could that be?*

Guilt wasn't an emotion Paul felt often, if at all. He did things, existing without consequence for his actions, and never being held accountable for them. And since he was thirsty, he finished it off without a second thought about me or what I might need.

I pursed my lips, looking around at the area we were in, hoping for a water source. Everything around us was frozen, and I knew I hadn't seen a creek since leaving the truck.

*What are we gonna do?*

For the moment, I was so thirsty I started shoveling handfuls of snow into my mouth. I'd heard someone at some point say it wasn't a good idea to do that, but I had no other ideas, and I needed it.

Figuring we could melt some more when we made camp, I only had to survive till then.

I waved at Paul to keep following me and figured if we passed by a creek on the way back, we could stop and have a refill there.

I hoped I saw one soon.

Even if I did have to break through the ice to get to the water, I didn't care. We needed it.

After what seemed like another bout of forever, we came upon a ravine that looked like it might have a creek in the bottom.

Figuring it was probably our only salvation, I stopped and crawled my way back to Paul to grab our canteen. I signed to him that I would go down into the ravine and check for water, and he needed to stay put while I went. It didn't appear to be that far, so I started working my way down the hill.

As I went further, the climb became steeper, though.

My footing slipped on my way down as the gradient

made a drastic change, and I started tumbling down the hill.

I couldn't stop myself and hoped I wouldn't hit a tree or end up hurting myself on the ice below. As I continued to gain speed, I started to panic. I hit the ice hard and it cracked, scraping my leg as I broke through and fell in.

I stood, ice up to my waist, with nothing underneath it.

After my heart stopped pounding and I could assess myself, disappointment set in.

*Where's the water? Why isn't there any water?*

I frowned, unable to wrap my exhausted brain around it. I should have been waist-deep in freezing water. I should have been soaking wet, and I wasn't.

*I don't understand. Why did it dry up?*

I slammed my fist against the ice surrounding me. Now I had a hurt leg, and I had to climb all the way back up the hill. It was a waste of time, and I was even thirstier than before. I wasted our time for nothing!

I rolled myself out of the hole and laid on the ice letting tears fall from my eyes as I let myself fall apart for a minute. I'd never felt more frustrated and defeated in my life. It was so overwhelming.

I wanted to give up.

I could hear Paul at the top of the hill, yelling. He was trying to get my attention.

I figured he'd probably watched me fall through the ice and was worried about me.

He yelled, "Ya ya ya Ya ya!"

Being deaf since birth, he was unable to form

coherent words, but he could make sounds when he wanted to. I don't know what made him think my name was Ya ya, but I knew he was trying to get my attention whenever he called it out.

I sat up to wave at him. He deserved to know I was okay so he wouldn't try to come down the hill. Lord knew it was going to take enough just to get *me* back up there.

I grimaced, feeling a wet, sticky sensation on my leg. It didn't feel like a horrible amount of wetness, so I figured I was cut, but wouldn't bleed to death.

I crawled onto my knees and started making my way up the hill. It took a little time, but it wasn't nearly as much time as I figured it'd take.

I felt grateful for that as I reached the top.

Paul pulled me into a hug, and I told him I was okay.

He signed to me, *'Did you get any water?'*

I sighed, signing to him that there wasn't any water, so we'd need to make some when we stopped to make camp.

He deflated, but I asked him to do the best he could to wait for it so we could walk as far as we could before then.

We began to walk again. I was trying not to think about the distance between us and the cabin.

In a short while, I was feeling pain in my leg, but not enough to slow me down. However, as more time passed, my leg was throbbing.

I started to notice how tired and sore I was, too. I

couldn't even bring myself to think about what we must look like as we made our way.

I was sure I looked tired, sore, crusty and sunburnt with squinted eyes.

Fully pitiful.

Looking at the sky, I figured we had to be getting into the evening by that point.

It'd be dark soon.

Just based on how I was feeling, I decided it'd be in our best interests to stop and make camp early. And, based on how dark it was already, it wasn't like we could walk much further.

I also knew I needed to check on my leg.

*Maybe if we get more rest we'll make better progress tomorrow,* I thought.

I turned and signed to Paul to let him know it was time to make camp.

He readily agreed to that.

We walked over to the treeline on the side of the road and started setting everything up.

He grabbed the tarp and started breaking the boughs off the nearby trees for our bed before laying out the sleeping bag.

I collected wood for our fire and started it up so we could thaw some food and melt some snow for water.

I grabbed the little pot from Paul's sled and piled it with snow.

We created sitting spots in the snow with more boughs so we could sit without our shoes, and let them dry out.

They were soaking wet from our sweating feet and

snow falling in at the tops, and a little frozen in the toes.

I grabbed a jar of pork and put it near the fire, but not too close because I was worried it would break from the heat.

I did not want us to have to eat glass again.

The smoke coming off of the fire stung our already sensitive eyes, but we only cared about the warmth.

It felt so good, we didn't care about anything else.

I took a moment to appreciate that fire. It was the best thing in the world.

As soon as there was enough water in the pot for both of us, I threw a handful of snow into it so it was cool enough for drinking. I cringed at the smoky flavor since it'd gotten ash in it, but it would hydrate us, and that was what really mattered.

I let Paul drink as much as he wanted first. There was a touch left when he'd finished, so I downed the rest and started refilling the pot with more snow. We needed to make sure we could fill our canteens for tomorrow.

I told Paul to continue filling the pot while I went to find more wood. It wasn't difficult, so before long I was settled back at the fire. I waited till I was warm enough before removing my snow pants to check on my leg.

It felt so sore I almost didn't want to see it. It made me nervous to think of how bad it could be.

My long johns were dark and crusted with blood under my knee and down my shin. I grabbed the cuff of my long johns and pulled to see how bad it was.

It hurt so bad pulling the cloth away after it had already crusted and scabbed.

Thankfully, it didn't start bleeding again. I figured that was a good sign.

I washed the area to find the wound and saw it was a cut right under my knee. That's why it was so painful. Every time I bent my knee, it was reopening the cut.

Even though it was a pretty big gash, it was only oozing a little. I looked at Paul who was grimacing at it, but there was nothing I could do about it. I didn't even feel worried.

I pulled the leg of my long johns down and prayed it was clean and wouldn't get infected. And most importantly: I could still walk in the morning.

I stared into the fire for a while, trying not to think about how we'd gotten where we were, or what we'd gone through to get there. I especially didn't want to know how long it was going to take us to get back.

I could only sit blankly.

I was pretty sure Paul felt just as blank and numb as I did. We sat there soaking, in the warmth for as long as we possibly could. It was completely dark out by the time I realized the fire was dying down, and we were almost out of wood to burn.

I sighed, looking up at the sky. The aurora in red, green, orange, purple, and white danced above our heads. It took my breath away with its beauty.

The stars were also enormous and bright. I couldn't remember the stars being that big at any other point in my life.

It was like I could reach out and touch them.

I pointed up so Paul knew to look. It hurt him to look up for some reason. I could see by the slow, deliberate movement of his head. But when he did, I watched his mouth drop.

It was funny to see such a look on his face, and I laughed. The whole scene made me feel better, even if it was just a little bit.

I grabbed my boots and got up to go to bed. I was determined to get as much rest as possible as I had no idea where we were, but I was praying against all odds we would make it back tomorrow.

Paul followed me, and we cuddled into the sleeping bag together.

I looked over at the dying fire and realized the jar of pork was still sitting there. We were so tired and dazed, we'd completely forgotten to eat.

*At least we have breakfast for tomorrow,* I thought, hoping it wouldn't freeze up again by the morning.

My eyes closed, and I finally had a night of sleep without dreams.

## ✦ 13 ✦

When I woke up, I felt warm. A novelty in this waste of a journey. I had no desire to pull my head out from under the sleeping bag.

The fleeting wish that I was back at the cabin, warm in my bed, came as a passing glance through my mind, and I wanted desperately for everything to be normal and alright. If everything was fine, that meant we'd made it back, and I wouldn't have to worry about us surviving for a while.

I finally pulled my head out of the bag to find the tarp pressing down on top of us. We'd gotten a fresh blanket of snow overnight. The tarp was heavy, and some of it had fallen down.

I looked over and saw my boots covered in snow, which meant they'd probably be frozen. I decided to start a fire to warm them, but when I reached to dust them off, only one of my boots appeared.

I dug a little deeper, thinking it was probably still covered, only to find it was not there.

*How can this be?* I thought.

I looked by the fire, thinking perhaps in my exhaustion, I'd only grabbed one as we were going to bed. I didn't see it there, but noticed the fire and the jar of meat had been covered by the snow. I figured the meat probably froze again, but this seemed pretty trivial in comparison to one of the most important pieces of my attire being lost.

*What happened to my boot?* I had to wonder, but more than that, a stranglehold of panic gripped me and started to squeeze.

I wouldn't be able to keep going without my boot. I couldn't walk through the snow without it. My toes would freeze off!

I woke Paul and signed to him, asking him if he'd seen me move my boot the night before.

He signed back, telling me I had moved them both before bed.

I frowned, sitting in the sleeping bag and racking my brain, trying to remember what I must have done with it.

Paul tapped my shoulder to get my attention before pointing out a pair of animal tracks right next to us under the tarp. The fresh snow hadn't covered them, so they must have happened pretty early in the night and we were so tired we didn't hear the animal come by.

My eyes went wide. I knew those tracks. Dad taught us all about the different animals we could find in the wilderness.

A wolverine had come through our camp.

*That must be what happened to my boot!*

I was six inches from a panic attack right then. I needed my boot. I could not safely get the two of us out of the woods if one of us had to walk around without something protecting our feet.

The biggest problem was the fact that the tracks beyond the tarp had been buried in the snow. There was no way for me to track its direction without them.

There was no choice, then.

I signed to Paul, telling him I needed to borrow his boot so I could go find mine.

He seemed perfectly content to stay warm and cozy in the sleeping bag, and allowed me to go out looking for it.

I started with small circles around our camp. I could only hope the wolverine dropped it on its way and left it somewhere close by. On top of that, I hoped it wouldn't take long to find because I didn't want to stay out longer than necessary.

It was the bloody boot, too. If, by some miracle the creature dropped it, I could only hope it hadn't torn it apart to eat the blood off.

*God, I could really use another miracle right about now!*

I walked in circles around our camp for what seemed like ages.

At one point, I decided it might be a good idea to at least start a fire to get some food and water going. If we were going to be stuck out here, we might as well make the most of it while I scoured the forest floor looking for my boot.

I walked back over to my brother to tell him the plan. He nodded, and I got to work on the fire, making a new dry little area for Paul to sit on while I borrowed his boot.

While he got situated, I went back to searching for my missing boot in the surrounding forest.

That little bit of normalcy of making a fire was all I could do to distract myself from not fully freaking out. My insides were a mess of fear and worry that I wouldn't find it, and we'd have to move on without it. Or worse, split up and hope for the best with the limited supplies we had.

The idea that we could have already been on the road and walking toward the cabin was the icing on the cake.

Here we could be moving, making some progress, but we're stuck here because some stinking animal took my boot!

I wandered for hours looking for anything that might be close to boot shaped. I continued to get further and further away from Paul and the fire as I went, but I occasionally brought wood back to my brother so he could keep the fire going.

He'd already opened the jar of pork and had been slowly picking at the pieces that thawed.

I had a bite once when I came back with wood, but my whole body felt so horrible from the unwitting emotions coursing through me, it almost made me sick eating any more.

I told him to keep eating while I went back out to search.

It was well into the day before I saw a lump in the snow that looked unusual compared to all of the other lumps I'd come across that ended up being rocks and logs. There was a green tinge that was out of place under the snow.

I held my breath.

*It can't be,* I thought, walking over to it and dusting the snow off.

I gasped. There it was, my boot. It was completely intact, and I picked it up like it was the greatest gift I'd ever received. I couldn't believe it was there.

I could only guess why the wolverine had dragged it off and left it, but I was so grateful for that, too.

I looked back in the direction I'd left Paul and figured it was probably a few hundred yards away from him and our little camp. The chances of me finding it were so small, I didn't even want to try and figure it out.

*Miracle, indeed,* I thought, thanking God profusely on my way back to the fire.

Relief washed over me as I continued to look it over, still finding nothing wrong with it. It was positively frozen solid, but nothing some time next to the fire wouldn't solve.

I rushed back, excited by my find and the fact that I could get both of us home safely now that I had both boots.

Paul looked cozy sitting in the sleeping bag next to the fire, eating away at the jar of pork.

He looked just as excited as I felt when he saw I had my boot in hand.

I explained to him the plan I had. I told him we

were going to thaw my boot before packing up and getting as far as we could before night fell again.

'*Will we make it home tonight?*' he signed, and I explained to him that I didn't know.

And it was true. I had no idea how far we'd come or how much walking we still had left to do.

He sighed, understanding I couldn't have the answers to those things, and we sat around the fire in silence, waiting for my boot to thaw as the day crept away.

I knew we wouldn't be making it very far, leaving in the middle of the day like we were. The sun was already above the horizon, and the snow was soft and difficult to walk through.

Paul looked at me after a while and asked if we could get moving. He was getting impatient, as was I.

I also knew he wanted to be home since day three of us being out in the cold and winter when Dad swore it was only going to take us a few days to make the whole trip.

I grabbed my boot and moved the sides and the tongue around to be sure it wouldn't kill me to walk around in it, and it seemed thawed enough. I signed to Paul that we could pack up and move out.

We grabbed the rest of our things and packed them onto the sleds. We walked out of the trees and onto the road, where the sun was so bright it stung our still-sensitive eyes.

The pain grated on my nerves as we pushed and pulled the sleds through the snow. I knew we had to keep moving if we were going to make any headway at all before nightfall.

Still, it was too easy to want to sit down and not get back up.

As the day continued to pass, Paul started showing signs of one of his fits. I knew if he got too angry, upset, or frustrated, something might happen, but our lack of progress for the day seemed to be weighing on him most, and there was really nothing I could do about that.

I didn't lose my boot on purpose to keep us out longer.

We both knew the cabin, our home, was not that far away, but as it had the entire trip, the snow was slowing us down and holding us back.

That was probably the most frustrating thing of all for me.

Paul burst out, yelling.

It was so sudden, I jumped. I turned to look, only to watch him start throwing supplies off his sled. I dropped the reins on my own sled and ran back to stop him.

I signed, '*What are you doing?*'

He signed back in angry, jerky motions, '*We'll make better time if we don't have to carry so many supplies!*'

I blinked at him. Sure, I could understand his anger and frustration. I'd been feeling it since day one. But we needed to deal with it and keep going.

The supplies were the whole reason we were out in the wilderness.

I shook my head, signing to him that he needed to

keep these things on his sled, and we were going to be okay.

I reached down to grab the sleeping bag and the grain to put them back, but he pushed me away, before cocking back and punching me square in the nose.

I landed on my butt in the snow as blood gushed red and bright out onto the sparkly white wasteland.

Shocked, I sat there for a moment before searing pain slammed into my senses. I could barely breathe as my face started to throb.

Thankfully, the bleeding stopped almost as soon as it'd gushed onto the snow.

I looked up at my brother, and he was staring back at me with tears in his eyes. I started to cry, too, hopelessness filling my chest.

Grabbing a handful of snow to put on my nose, I slowly got up and used the snow to wash away as much blood as possible.

I could barely think, but I was sure he'd broken my nose.

After cleaning up as much as I could, I looked at him and signed, asking if we could keep moving.

He nodded, but he told me nothing was going back on his sled.

I frowned at him and asked if I could put the stuff on my sled.

He signed back, '*No.*'

I bit my lip, afraid to reach for it or try to put any of it on my sled. I knew he wasn't in the right frame of mind, so there wasn't much more I'd be able to do.

I gently reminded him we needed the sleeping bag,

at least. I didn't care about anything else if he didn't want to carry it.

He said no. He reasoned we were going to keep walking until we made it home. There were no other options.

I pursed my lips. I didn't want to leave it behind. My gut screamed at me to reach for it and pick it up, but my head and nose were throbbing, and my eyes still burned. So, I turned and started walking.

I left a small piece of us behind.

## ❧ 14 ❧

We walked and walked, stopping on occasion to rest our sore, aching bodies, and finding it more difficult to get back up and keep moving.

I realized the sun was beginning to set, and I still had no idea how close we were to home. At points, I'd see something that looked familiar to me, and it possibly meant we were getting closer, but I didn't know, and I couldn't guess.

Paul started crying as the sun set. He'd been talking to himself more frequently as the day passed.

I was scared to stop now. I wanted to start making camp, but we had no sleeping bag, and the temperature was dropping fast. As the sun finally set and the sky grew dark, the sinking conclusion we were not going to make it back to the cabin took over. We would not be making it home before we'd need to sleep.

I didn't want to attempt to find our way through the woods in the dark.

I stumbled to a stop and fell into the snow. I couldn't have gotten up if I wanted to.

Rolling over, I looked at Paul and signed for him, *'We have to stop. I can barely see in front of my face.'*

As begrudged as we both were, he agreed with me.

I watched him sit down by his sled as if the life had slipped from his body and the depressing thought of having to sleep in the snow without the sleeping bag seemed to crush us both.

We didn't have the energy to make a fire as the last bit of light left the sky, sinking behind the mountain tops. I pulled the tarp off of my sled, thankful, and cherished that small bit of protection we had, even though I knew it probably wasn't going to be enough.

I crawled over to Paul and laid it out, asking him to roll into it before I climbed in beside him.

It was so cold laying on top of the snow like that. We had no energy to gather tree boughs to lay on the snow to help protect us, and on top of that, we were still in our snow gear drenched from our sweat and melted snow. Before, we had been relying on the fires we built at night to dry us out, and now, we were wet and trying to keep warm without one.

As the temperature continued to drop, I could feel my body temperature dropping along with it. My clothes began to harden like ice in the cold.

My whole body throbbed and ached, though the pain seemed distant as we laid there. The pulse of blood passing through my bruised and battered tissue was weak and made me realize the extent of my exhaustion.

I was tired. Tired of life at that moment. Sick of

having to take care of everything and be strong for everyone. I didn't want to do anything anymore besides sleep. I could not even think of the next day and what it would take to keep going.

Paul trembled beside me. I was certain it was from the cold because I was beginning to shiver too.

I snuggled into him, and we both held each other tighter, hoping to stay warm, but I couldn't feel anything but the aching cold seeping into my bones.

As the hours passed, our shivering got progressively worse, to the point that the two of us were violently shaking, almost as if we were both having seizures. I'm not sure how long it was, but the muscles contracting from the relentless shivering pulled at my stomach and ribs with such force, it felt as though I was being ripped apart from the inside.

It felt like my kidneys were going to split and tear through my body. My chest ached, and I wanted to fold in on myself as I hugged Paul tighter, as tightly as I could. I prayed this would control my convulsions and provide him with some amount of heat.

I imagined he felt the same way. I felt so helpless. I did not want to cry, though, and make the pain worse.

My thoughts started to wander. I thought of Mom, and how the whole family we left behind must be wondering if we had died by now. With that thought, the sharp clarity that we *were* going to die stamped itself into my brain. That would mean Andy and Mom were going to die, too. If Paul and I couldn't bring them food, there was no way they'd make it through the winter here.

Like many times before, on this journey, I wondered if they were coming to find us, and if they would be here any minute. But that thought died quickly because I knew if we had not seen them by now, they were not coming.

*Perhaps someone will find our bodies in the summer when the snow melts or maybe the animals will get to us first.*

Although these thoughts were concerning to me, I also felt detached from them. Like they were happening close to my head, but outside of it. Almost like they were being whispered in my ear by someone else, and they didn't belong to me.

*I wonder what time it is.*

I knew we'd been there for hours, but I couldn't be sure how much of the night slipped by already.

*Why am I not sleeping?*

All of a sudden, my thoughts cleared. I realized I felt warm and wasn't shivering anymore. Not only that, but Paul wasn't shivering anymore either!

I figured he was still asleep because I could hear soft, faint breathing. As I became more awake, I realized the sun must be close to rising because I could see sunlight creeping through the tarp.

A burst of excitement beat in my chest. *I can't believe we made it through the night!*

I felt the sun warming my limbs, and I could feel that warmth creeping up my legs, into my stomach, and soothing the aches and pains away.

I was so excited that I was ready to tackle the day. I wasn't going to waste any time. I knew if we got going early, we could probably make it home.

With excitement and the warm sun compelling me, I reached for my brother and began to shake him to wake him up. I knew he would be excited the sun was up and we would make it home today—

I GASPED and opened my eyes to total darkness. I was frozen in place, barely able to move my arms and legs. Even though I was no longer shivering, I was far from warm.

I couldn't feel anything anymore.

Worse, the sun was not up. I'd dreamt it. All of it.

Another horrible wave of panic washed over me as I realized I must have the beginnings of hypothermia. Everything about me felt like I'd been frozen to the ground in the night.

I started thrashing, trying to get my legs and arms to work. Paul was lying next to me, not moving a muscle. His breathing hadn't even changed with me thrashing around right next to him.

I finally forced myself onto my knees and threw off the tarp. It was still dark, but with a small touch of light in the sky, I realized that dawn was not that far off.

I grabbed Paul and started shaking him awake, for real this time. He didn't move at all, even when I pinched and pulled his cheeks and nose. It seemed like he was in a coma or knocked out.

I started to scream at him, knowing it wouldn't work, but it didn't matter. I would try anything to get him to wake up. Still, Paul continued to slip further and further away from me.

## 15

"No, Paul, c'mon! Please, please wake up!" I begged. A primal fear gripped my throat, and the tears fell for him, for us, for this whole stupid situation. I couldn't control it. The floodgates of everything I'd been bottling up and pushing away throughout our journey came spilling out of my body.

I grabbed his shoulders, head, and anything I could move and shake to try to get him to wake up. Shouting at him seemed useless, but I did it anyway. Screaming felt better than nothing. Clawing and grabbing at his clothes, prying at his eyelids.

*Anything, please. Just anything! Don't leave me alone, please!*

If there was ever a time I had some words for God, it was then. If God gave me the strength I needed to wake up from this, he needed to take care of my brother too. I couldn't do it without him. I couldn't move on without him. Even if we couldn't talk to each other. Even if he'd caused this situation for us where I woke up nearly frozen to death. Even if we were meant to die out here with Mom and Dad and Andy, he was not allowed to die before we made it back.

I held Paul's cold hands and rubbed at his arms to move the blood around. I picked up his head and thumped on his chest to see if that would work, but he wasn't budging. He would not wake up.

The tears fell over my cheeks in rivers, now. I screamed. I didn't care. It was dark and cold and this was something I couldn't deal with.

"God, please, don't leave me out here alone. Please! I just wanna go home. I want me and Paul to make it back home. Please, please, please. Work for me just this one time, please!"

I sobbed, continuing to beat Paul's chest as I laid there and cried.

After that, it was like I'd released a dam. Tears kept flowing, and I cried for everything that was wrong with my life and the world at that moment. For my family possibly starving to death because we didn't make it back in time; for our strange, horrible life and being stuck out in the wilderness; for Daisy and our animals; for my dumb luck; for Paul; everything I could think of, I let myself cry for. I didn't hold back, either. I even cried for what I knew would need to happen next.

When we returned home, I knew I would have to initiate some sort of change if I was ever going to feel safe again. It was terrifying to think about. I let it flow from my body, anyway. I couldn't hold onto it any longer.

I didn't want to be responsible for any of it anymore.

As I sobbed into Paul's chest, a hand laid itself over the back of my head. I gasped, and my head shot up to look at him. He was looking at me through slitted, sleepy eyes, but very much alive.

I let out a choked cry before frantically rubbing and shaking him, trying to get him to stand. Finally with his eyes fully opened, he started processing the situation. The color was just peaking on the horizon as Paul took his first deep breath, coming back to life.

I pulled at him, getting him to sit up. Standing on my own shaky, frozen legs, I began to jump and stomp around. Even though it was mostly for survival, it also felt like a celebration. Paul was alive! I was alive! We'd made it through another night in this Godforsaken place! I was so grateful I cried to the sky, to God for listening to me.

I grabbed his arm and pulled, encouraging him to stand and jump around with me. We needed to get our blood pumping and our bodies warm.

He stood and mimicked me as best he could. I'd had more time to move as I struggled to wake him, so it wasn't quite as bad as his stiff form. Our clothes were so frozen that it was difficult to move around in them. Our boots had frozen on our feet and felt like what I imagined a cast would feel like, unmoving and firm, but unfortunately, our boots were loose and rubbing against our ankles and peeling skin off.

I'd gotten accustomed to this since my boots were

already too small and had been chafing my feet and ankles for several days.

Still, my brother and I looked at each other as the sun peeked over the trees, and I knew we'd been blessed with one more day. Maybe it was the day we'd finally make it home.

To be fair, it would have to be. My whole body had been rubbed raw right down to my soul. But I was lighter, too. Everything that had been weighing on me had been cried out. I felt free and capable. I wouldn't even entertain the idea of sleeping outside in the cold one more night.

I folded up the tarp, feeling renewed by our blessing. Things were crisp in the early morning, and it was easy to walk over the snow like it had been the first morning we left the cabin.

It was the same kind of hope, too. The kind where you know you could probably conquer a mountain in a day, even if it was completely unrealistic.

I didn't care. God was still on my side.

I grabbed Paul's hand and led him to his sled before grabbing mine.

My whole body was shaky and weak, and I felt dizzy and lightheaded. We hadn't eaten, and we were still a little frozen, but I knew we needed to take advantage of being awake.

Paul seemed a little shaky, himself. I signed to him, as best I could, that we needed to move until our bodies felt better and headed off. I knew he would follow me. After all we'd experienced, I think we had more trust in each other now than we'd had our whole lives. I had his back, and I knew he would have mine from here on out. But he needed to know we were still in danger.

We literally weren't out of the woods, yet.

Even though there was a nice crust on the snow, we still stumbled and fell as we went. I would not let us stop, not even for a moment to quench our thirst with some boiled water.

We just scooped up some snow and ate it to keep the feeling at bay. I didn't want to lose even an ounce of the day we had ahead of us.

I COULDN'T SAY how long we'd been walking for, but it felt like ages. I'd turn around and wave at Paul to keep coming, signing every once in a while that we were getting close.

I couldn't say how I knew that, but I had to believe we wouldn't have to risk freezing to death for a second night in a row. I was so determined to believe this that I was pushing us way beyond what I had for all of the other days we'd been out on our own.

After several hours, when the sun was high in the sky and the snow glittered in the light, I saw the marker I put out on the first day of our journey. It was nearly covered in snow, but I knew that tree, and that one close by it, and the pine with the weird branches!

It was a sign of hope that we could feasibly make it back by night. After seeing that marker, I was so determined that I was going to get us back to our nice, safe, warm cabin if it took everything I had.

I started pushing us harder.

After what I thought was probably another hour by how the shadows moved on the ground, I could see a dark lump in the road up ahead. It was the Dodge. It had to be. I couldn't imagine anything else that big taking up that much space on the road.

That meant we were only a few miles away.

I beamed, pointing it out to Paul. He squinted and took a moment to process, but when he understood what it was, he also seemed to gain a second wind, and we started making significant progress as we trudged on.

Taking in the scene, it was the first time I could actually appreciate the area. The sky was clear, and the world was silent. Not even a bird was twittering in the trees. The snow crunched under our feet, and the air was crisp.

I couldn't help but feel a change in the air. We were nearly home. Safety and warmth were within my grasp.

Paul and I continued forward. Our labored breathing cut into the silence as we pushed through the snow with the very last of our strength.

When we reached the truck, I started to yell. I thought if we yelled enough, the sounds of our voices would carry over the quiet, snow-covered earth, and they would hear us.

I wanted so desperately to see the rest of my family alive and well, that I think I let it blind me to every other feeling and possibility there was. I'm sure my brother felt the same.

Even though he couldn't hear me shouting, Paul realized what I was doing, and he began to yell the best he could as we walked along. He was more attuned to things than I gave him credit for, but I appreciated him trying all the same.

It felt so close, yet so far. I was so tired. I think we both were exhausted by then, but we kept moving and kept yelling. I didn't even care if I lost my voice at that point. At the rate we were going, we'd make it back to the cabin before dark.

About a mile from the cabin, I looked up and saw someone in the distance coming toward us. A woman in a brown coat, which was much too large to be her own, was there on the road. I started sobbing as I realized it was Mom running through the snow as fast as she could with Dad's coat on.

*She's alive!* Our work and suffering and horrible turmoil were worth something.

I dropped the rope to the sled and started stumbling toward her as quickly as I could. Even though the snow was still nearly impossible to run through, I dug in and stumbled, anything I could do to get to her.

Wiping at the tears that would not stop falling, I looked behind me to see Paul had left his sled, too. He was right behind me, yelling the way he always did. Not coherent, but the tone showed that he was incredibly excited and was probably yelling his version of "Mom". His face was lit up and full of light.

I knew he was as happy as I was to see our mom right then.

I looked back at Mom, who was still trying to get

through the snow as fast as she could; she kept stumbling, but she refused to stop. As she drew near, I could hear faint sobbing through her breathing. It hurt so much to see her like that. But all I could think about was reaching her. I just wanted my mom. I wanted her so bad that it hurt not to touch her and hug her right then.

Mom reached us, and I threw myself into her arms. We were all sobbing and hugging and tired, but it didn't matter.

We made it.

We survived.

## 16

E ven though it was just a sleeping bag on a ratty, used mattress, my bed was the softest and warmest thing I'd ever felt. I barely left it since returning to the cabin. Mom and Dad allowed Paul and me the rare chance to rest, which I couldn't have been more grateful for. I didn't want to do anything but feel the safety of the cabin, and to rest.

Something still nagged at me, though. I could feel it in the lump in my throat, and it continued to rise and choke me.

It had been several days since we'd made it back. Mom helped us drag the sleds in after we managed to stop crying. Andy had been waiting in the doorway when we walked into view of our camp.

Dad trudged out to meet us and helped us inside. I couldn't tell what he thought when he saw the supplies we'd brought back, but I couldn't try to rectify things at that moment. A slight twinge of guilt sprung up, but it didn't compare to my excitement and the onset of exhaustion as I knew we would be sleeping in our nice, safe cabin.

"Sapph, tell me—"

"Shh," Mom silenced Dad before he had a chance to finish his sentence.

I watched the exchange, feeling detached from it. I could only imagine how they must have fought while Paul and I were gone. Dad usually got angry when things were out of his control, and I was certain Mom spent many of the nights we were gone sleeplessly wondering if we'd frozen to death out in the wilderness.

For once, Dad didn't argue with her. Whether it was because he could see that Paul and I were at our tipping points, or because they'd already agreed to hold back all the questions until we had a chance to settle in, I couldn't be sure.

I sighed my relief all the same.

Mom took our coats and set them close to the fire to dry out some of the sweat. I knew they really needed to be washed, but if I needed to go back outside, I couldn't without my coat. I'd have to suffer with a dirty one.

The rest of our family gave Paul and me a chance to change clothes and wash off in the small corner room. Nothing could beat being somewhat clean, and Mom took the time to dress the gash in my knee before sending us to bed.

Now, I was rested and hydrated. Even if our food was mostly grain and jarred meat, I was now eating enough to feel energized and capable. It was way better than the little we'd been eating on the trail as we were barely scraping by in survival mode.

But still, just a few days ago, I'd nearly died and lost my brother in the process. The freezing cold had almost taken both of us, and there would have been nothing I could have done about it had I not woken up.

I felt sad, happy, angry, and so confused all in one. I knew in my heart of hearts it was not over. We still had such a long winter ahead of us and had barely brought enough to make it more than a few weeks or a month. Someone would have to go back and get more grain, and I knew, without a doubt, I would be that someone.

But I did not want to think about that. I wanted to soak up the warmth and feel the cold in my bones seep away, feel the ache wash through my body as it recovered from what it just went through.

I felt so weak and so drained. I was still in awe that we survived. I still did not know how.

I thought about each day and played the events over and over again in my mind, wondering if in the end we would make it and if that trip had been for nothing. But I moved on from that thought and looked into the future, wondering how we would get out of this mess.

It brought up many questions for me. I wondered if things would have been different if I got us moving sooner than when we had left the Ford. I knew I couldn't be blamed for the boot incident, but I couldn't help thinking about how much further we could have gone had I not taken hours to find it in the snow.

And more than that, I wondered if we would have

SURVIVE

been spared that near-death experience if someone had come out to find and help us.

*Why didn't Mom and Dad come out to look for us?*

The thought haunted me since I'd returned home. We were gone twice as long as we should have been according to Dad's estimations. Surely, as the fourth day rolled around and we weren't home, they should have sent someone out to at least make sure we weren't dead.

We were all starving, after all. *Why would you wait for food to run out before checking that your one chance of survival wasn't trapped out in the wilderness, or had been eaten by a wolf or something else just as horrible?*

I couldn't understand it.

Through all of my own personal puzzling, I decided it must have been Dad who'd convinced Mom not to go looking for us. They must have put a time limit on it. If we hadn't returned after a certain amount of time, I bet they would have come looking. That only made me angrier.

I know what I told God I would do if we were allowed to make it out of there alive, but leaving my mom wasn't possible for me. Who was I without her? I couldn't imagine.

Instead, I decided to talk to Mom and ask her to leave Dad if and when we got out of here. Let her know we could not go through this anymore.

Naturally, I knew she could see his malicious behavior and what it was doing to all of us. *She had to care about her own kids more than him, right?*

And if she did not want to leave, then that would be the moment I would know it was time to go alone.

145

I knew I was justified, and asking that of her felt like a reasonable request. Playing the last few days over in my mind, I couldn't help questioning who would want to stay with a man who endangered their children to such an extent. *Who would actively leave space in the future for something like this to happen to their family again?*

I chuckled as I thought of all the horrible things he had put us through over the years already.

*How can I laugh at that? I'm losing my mind, I know it,* I thought.

EVEN IN THE days since returning, Dad hadn't said much to me. I wondered if it was Mom's doing or if he was trying to work through what we were going to do with the supplies we were able to bring back.

I couldn't care less, though. He could vanish in the snow, for all I cared. It was his fault Paul and I nearly died out there. *Why should I care for someone who clearly didn't care about me?*

The idea of me no longer caring for my dad felt strange. Like, I knew some ideal told me I had to care for him because he was my dad and a part of my family, and everyone should care for their family members, but I lost that for him.

I'd circulate that thought several times to make sure I was convinced of those feelings and not just mad at him for bringing us out here, but the more I thought about it, the more sure I became. Any love I had was quickly slipping away into the frigid wilderness.

I also took the time to visit the warm, joyful feeling

I had when I was on the cusp of death. I knew that feeling had to be God's Light. I knew I was being given a choice on what to do next. That I could have run into that warmth and been wrapped blissfully in sunshine and happiness forever if I wanted. And for a minute there, I was truly excited about it. I wanted that reprieve.

But it was a choice, and my life was also on the line. I had to believe God gave me this second chance for a reason. It was not my time to go, and I think God was making sure I knew that by allowing Paul to live, as well.

It was the only way I could think through it all and have it make sense.

MOM WAS MILLING some grain on the other side of the cabin when Dad walked through the front door and kicked off his boots.

"Sapphire, get out of bed and tell me what happened out there. I've thought about it these last few days, and I can't figure out why it took you so damn long to get back here," he said.

I sat up. I wasn't surprised he finally decided to ask, and I heard Mom heave a sigh before wiping her hands on her pants and turning to join us. It seemed she also wanted to know but was annoyed Dad asked.

It didn't really matter to me. Talking about the nightmare was the same as playing it over and over in my mind as I had been. And they deserved to know what happened to us.

Since Paul couldn't really contribute, it was up to me to divulge everything, and I decided it would be a disservice to hold anything back. They deserved to know what kind of horrible journey their children were forced to endure without them.

When I got to the end of my story, Mom was crying quietly, and Dad had a thoughtful frown over his brow.

The nagging question continued to plague me. *Why didn't they come to find us after we'd been gone for so long?*

WHEN MY WONDERING sat with me long enough, I turned to Mom when it was just the two of us in the cabin.

"Mom, why didn't you or Dad come looking for us when it was starting to be too long for us to be out there?" I asked.

I think she'd been expecting me to ask because she sighed and continued working on her washing.

"I did try, Sapphire. It's not that I didn't want to. I started walking, and the snow kept crumbling beneath me. I didn't make it far at all before turning back. It was just impossible to get through it."

I blinked at her back, watching her every movement for some indication of guilt, but none was there.

Though I felt a slight bit better knowing that she had wanted to, and made something of an attempt, there was a sudden rolling sickness in the pit of my stomach.

She felt a need as indicated by her going out there,

yet she couldn't even follow through to make sure her kids were alive?

Even worse, I couldn't believe Dad hadn't stepped up to go in her place. That he would leave something difficult like that to Mom.

I didn't say anything in response to her. I couldn't fathom any of it. So, I sat in my anger and confusion instead. *Weren't Paul and I worth anything to them?*

I wanted to be, more than anything, but I also knew this was exactly the reason I needed to leave.

Right now, I didn't have a choice in the matter if I wanted to protect myself.

"SAPPH, it's about time to make another trip," Dad said to me after a few weeks of being home from the first horrible trip.

I didn't like that news at all, and I thought about my options.

"This time, you're coming with me instead of Paul. I think it'll be easier now that you know what you're doing out there. You can prevent anything bad from happening, since you have already experienced it."

I remained silent, stewing in my bad luck.

Dad cleared his throat. "You're strong, Sapph. You can handle this better than anyone here."

While I knew some part of me should have appreciated the pep talk and been proud of the fact that Dad found some value in my strength, there was nothing about it that made me believe it. I was always a means to his end.

A wave of hot, boiling anger, like I'd felt when I was out on the trail, spread from my gut out to my head and limbs. I hid my clenched fists, though I knew my face was burning in my rage.

"Okay," I agreed because I knew there was no other way around it.

I WAS FORCED into two more trips like the first over our winter in the Yukon. They weren't as bad as the first trip out with Paul, since I knew what was coming. And a trail formed in the snow from our walks, which meant it was a little easier to get through each time we went.

Eventually, the jars of meat ran out, and all we could bring back was animal grain. Mom tried to be creative with it, but after a while, it was just bread.

I noticed my clothes getting bigger and looking like drapes over my form after several months. I didn't have the energy to handle much of anything, either.

The only thing that wasn't shrinking was my belly, which grew this weird bulge and felt tight under my skin. Looking at the rest of my family, I noticed their clothes were bigger, too, and their skin looked pale and slack.

Even without a mirror, I knew I probably looked as unhealthy as they did, and it scared me. My daily prayers turned into pleas for winter to come to an end as soon as possible.

.  .  .

I COULDN'T BE sure how much time passed, or even what month or day it was anymore. The days had been getting longer, and the sun felt better and better each day that I woke up with it streaming onto my face from the window.

Today, the sun was so warm that small drips were falling from the roof and trees as the snow melted.

It was so warm that as the day passed, the snowmelt sounded like rain as it fell from the roof to the ground and gathered in large, icy pools.

So much melted, my heart sang. I couldn't attribute it to anything else. My prayers had finally been answered. Spring was coming, and it was only a matter of time before we could leave this place and never return.

No more wheat paste, wheat porridge, whole wheat "soup", or wheat sprouts.

The thought of good food made my stomach gurgle. I couldn't even say how we were going to get out with two broken trucks, but I knew Dad would find a way, so all I had to do was wait.

IF I HAD the chance to get Mom alone, today was the day I would talk to her about the future of our family and what getting out of here would mean for us. I knew she and Dad had been talking and planning something, but I was never privy to those conversations. Dad usually liked to keep us guessing when it came to our next moves.

But really, I wanted to give Mom a chance to prove

to me she had her children's best interests at heart. Especially mine.

While walking to the creek to get some more water for camp, I decided this was the best time. It was now or never.

"Mom, will you leave Dad when we get out of here?" I asked.

She frowned. "No, why would I do that?"

I guess I shouldn't have been surprised to hear that, but I stood on the path feeling stunned at how unbelievably blind she was. "After all of this, how could you not want to?"

"Sapphire, someday I will be all alone without my children, and I will have nobody to keep me company. You don't know what it's like to face something like that."

I wasn't sure how to respond through my confusion. I didn't understand why her loneliness outweighed the well-being of her own flesh and blood. I didn't care about that! What did that have to do with anything?

It was then I realized none of this mattered to Mom. Not the fact that we were starving and unhealthy, not the fact that Dad risked the lives of her family for the sake of a stupid whim, and not for the fact that we were regularly abused by him without any repercussions. And if her only care was in having someone around in the future, I wasn't going to care about her feelings if I left.

While her disregard hurt me and the ache in my chest grew as I began to process this new realization, I knew the truth now.

Mom would never leave the man who had and continued to cause us so much pain and misery. And I knew my choice, too.

"Mom, I will be leaving, then. I can't stay. I can never let myself have even the possibility of experiencing anything like this again. So, I have to leave."

I don't think Mom was expecting me to say that because she paused to stare at me for a moment. Then, she shrugged her shoulders like it was no big deal that I wanted to go off on my own at eleven years old. As if she did not believe I was actually going to do it.

She turned and continued walking toward the creek for our water run.

I watched her walk away. What more could I do? The lack of care or concern from my mom made my heart ache.

The fact that she couldn't see I had never been surer of anything in my life hurt me. I would have to take things into my own hands. I would leave no matter what I had to do in order to make my life better.

IT SEEMED like no time at all before the ground started to show through the snow. The air didn't have a chill to it anymore, and I could smell spring arriving. The scent of wet earth gave me even more hope than the melting snow had.

Now, I knew we were going to make it out.

I made a point to go out each day and feel the fresh air. The warm sun on my face made life bearable. I craved that small grace and the way it would melt some of my pain away. I imagined it was healthy for my skin, too, and I would take off my coat for a few spare minutes to get as much sunlight as possible.

I hadn't realized how cold I'd been without it.

The activities were sparse. We had a bunch of books we'd brought in over the summer, and I'd taken to reading them numerous times to kill some of my boredom. We could only have so much firewood, and resting was great for a little while, at least.

We'd had more fun when it was warm and I could go exploring in the woods.

But anything was better than being on the trail.

I'd taken to reading the huge stack of *Reader's Digest,* which the previous owners of the cabin left behind. There were at least one hundred of them, and I'd read each one front to back. Some, I'd even set aside and read through a second time.

I liked them because they had fun and interesting articles that made me lose track of time. And I liked keeping my mind busy most of all.

Most of the time, I spent ignoring my whirring thoughts of how I would get out of here and leave my family. It made me impossibly sad to think I wouldn't be around Mom or my brothers anymore, and I wondered if any of my other siblings felt that at any point while living with Mom.

But I was also angry. I knew I would have to figure out something soon since shortly we'd be out of the woods. Still, thinking about it was difficult.

. . .

THE DAY I woke up to barely any snow at all, I couldn't believe my eyes. The hated mushy slush was only visible under the trees where it was shady, which meant we'd probably be able to drive out of here.

*How* was another thing entirely.

It did not stop me from being excited by the prospect.

I spent the day exploring the puddles of snowmelt and mud like they were a brand new scientific discovery. They were amazing to me, honestly. I'd skip from one puddle to the next like a game of hopscotch. I knew this was the turning point for me and my family. I just had to wait to hear the plan Dad had for us.

I took my time heading back to camp when the sun started to set. The more time I could spend away from camp, the better. It was getting stuffy and funky from our days of unwash.

Sure, we had the sponge bath in the back, but nothing compared to an actual shower.

Mom was sitting on the edge of their bed and Dad was sitting in his normal spot by the barrel stove. The stove was off for the first time all winter, and I knew they'd come up with a way to get us out.

"When are we leaving?" I asked as I sat down on my bed across the room.

Dad looked at me with surprise, and I wondered if he thought I'd wanted to stay out here.

*As if!*

He took a breath and nodded his head. "Well, Sapphire, I believe this snow will be gone by the end of the week. So, at that point I thought we could either walk or ride out."

I frowned. What did he mean by *'ride out?'*

"Do you have a way to fix the truck? What does 'ride out' mean?" I asked.

He scoffed. "No. The trucks are down till we can get to town and get some parts. No, we have a motorcycle in the back shed."

My eyes grew wide, and I felt my eyebrows climb up my forehead. How could I have forgotten the motorcycle? He'd brought it last summer, and it'd been there this whole time. I didn't even realize it worked, considering he never used it after bringing it out here.

I looked at Mom, and she smiled at me reassuringly.

Dad cleared his throat. "We'll head out to get parts for the truck as soon as we're able."

THE REMAINING days went by in a blur. One morning, I woke up to rustling around in the cabin and saw Mom and Dad getting ready for the morning.

She noticed I was awake and smiled at me before whispering, "Sapphire, you are going with your dad today to see if you can get out to get some parts."

My heart leaped into my throat. "Are we walking all that way?"

Mom chuckled, "No. You guys are going to ride. Dad thinks the road is clear enough to ride through."

I beamed at her, but inside I was shrieking with joy. *Finally!*

I jumped out of bed and rushed to put on my clothes. Everything looked pretty dirty and dingy at this point, so I grabbed something that seemed decent enough.

Dad led the way out to the shed behind the cabin. We took a moment to look at the bike, assessing if it would run or not.

It'd been sitting there all winter, so even I had to wonder.

Since Dad fixed up the Ford after pulling it out of the river back in Grove, I trusted him to fix whatever vehicle we had around. And the motorcycle seemed easy enough. It was certainly less complicated than a truck engine.

Dad had me grab things and hold tools for him as he tuned the bike. We spent all day working on it, but I didn't care. I'd do anything I could to get that thing running and get out of the forest.

When he finally got it running, it was the loudest, most incredible sound I'd heard in months. I had no idea how silent our little world had been until it'd been broken by the rev of the motorcycle.

While it kind of hurt and made my ears ring, I never wanted that sound to stop. It was the closest I'd come to freedom since being trapped in the Yukon. That was huge for me.

"Alright, Sapph, looks like she's good to go," Dad shouted over the engine.

I cheered and danced around for a minute. "Are we leaving, then?" I shouted back.

He turned the engine off and turned to me. "We'll

leave at first light tomorrow. We've wasted too much daylight today to make it out and back in time."

I nodded, still feeling the ringing in my ears.

While part of me didn't want to go with Dad, I really wanted to get out of the woods. I wanted to be able to go further than I had gone in months and not have to walk to get there for once.

I watched as Dad made some final adjustments to the bike before I walked back to the cabin to see what Mom was doing.

When I walked inside, Mom was humming to herself. She seemed happier today than I'd seen her all winter, which was a good sign she was also ready to get out of the woods.

I noticed a couple of bags in the corner, and when she saw it was me walking inside, she pointed to them. "Those are what you and Dad will be taking with you when you head out."

They were supplies in case Dad and I were gone a couple of days.

I didn't want to think about that '*in case*' statement. I could only think about what was going to go right for us now.

Everything had to go according to plan because as soon as I got out of here and knew my family was some-what safe, I would be heading out on my own.

# EPILOGUE

While I should have known we wouldn't be heading back to Grove, the fact that we didn't, made me panic. Part of my escape plan relied on the fact that I would see my friends again, and that the pastor would take pity on me and would give me shelter for a while until I got back on my feet.

Beyond the fact that I desperately missed my friends, I knew we had a house there, and it made sense we would need a place to launch from again. The cabin wasn't going to work well for that.

Once my family left the cabin, we ended up going further into the Canadian backwoods to stay in a trailer close to my aunt's house. Well, Mom and Dad were staying in a trailer. Paul, Andy and I each had our own tents set up outside of the trailer.

Like all of the other places we'd been, it was still secluded and offered little hope of a new escape for me. I knew I couldn't give up hope, though. I promised God

I would make a better life for myself, and I had to be firm about it.

A COUPLE of months went by with me learning about the people and the area, and formulating a new plan. Each day, I would rack my brain on how I could escape my situation and get out. When my perfect plan finally came together, I sent a quick prayer and begged for a swift exit.

It wasn't easy to get in and out of where we'd set up camp. I think Dad did that on purpose so we wouldn't have very many people coming around and crossing our path. It seemed like Dad was even more paranoid about that possibility since we'd left the woods.

On one side of our camp was a river, which you could cross to get out, or you had to walk miles out the other side if you didn't have a 4x4. And that was to get into the nearest town.

There wasn't much there, and it seemed even fewer people, but that meant it was easy to meet the locals and get to know all of them.

I was raised to be a good and polite child and that worked in my favor. I knew everyone in town liked me, and if I asked, I knew any one of them would help me if they could.

With that in mind, it was time to put my plan into place and start contacting people.

. . .

THE PHONE RANG, and my heart thudded against my ribcage. I was nervous. Even though I was calling one of my older sisters, I still couldn't tell if she'd be on my side and willing to help me.

"Hello?" came a feminine voice after the third ring.

"Jenn? It's me, Sapphire," I answered.

"Oh, Sapph. What a surprise! I wasn't expecting to hear from you."

My heart sank. *Maybe I shouldn't have called. This was a mistake. Of course I should have given her a heads up.*

I cleared my throat and stuffed my runaway thoughts. "Yeah, I know. I didn't know where else to turn."

She paused on the other end, and I wondered what she was going to say.

I heard some shuffling around in the background before she spoke again. "Sapph, I have Adam here with me, too. What's going on?"

"Hi, Sapphire."

I smiled at the sound of my brother-in-law's voice. "Hi, Adam. Thanks for getting on. I actually have a lot to say. Do you have time?"

They agreed to all the time I needed, and I relaxed a little. Jenn had always been one of my more maternal sisters. Even though she and Adam were recently married, I knew she'd come through and do what she could for me.

I took a breath and told them everything. I told them about being trapped in the Yukon all winter and how Dad sent me and Paul out alone to face death while we were all on the verge of starvation. I explained how

I'd asked Mom to leave him, and how she'd completely disregarded me, and how we were now back into the same routine of staying in really secluded places and would probably end up moving on soon.

They listened patiently to me and asked an occasional question along the way. And when I finished my story, I took a breath in anticipation of what was about to come next.

"So, anyway," I continued, "I want to get away from them. I want a better life for myself. Will you help me?"

"Oh my gosh, Sapphire, of course! You can come here and stay with us in Oregon, and we'll take care—"

"No," I interrupted my sister. It was incredibly kind of her, and maybe I would take her up on that in the future, but I had a plan. "Thank you for your offer. I really appreciate it, but I actually have a plan you can help me with. It's why I called you."

I could hear some mumbling on the other end of the line, and I waited. I assumed they were talking things through with each other, which was fine. I wanted them to be comfortable with all of this too.

"Are you sure, Sapph? It's really no trouble for us to stop by and pick you up. We don't want you to be there any longer than you have to," Adam explained, and I heard Jenn agree in the background.

I thought about it for a moment. If I was at Jenn's, that might make Mom and Dad think they could go there too. That we'd be traveling to a new place as a family like we always did. I didn't want to give them that option or put that kind of burden on Jenn.

I nodded to myself. "Yeah, I'm sure. Maybe someday

we can discuss it, but right now, I don't want to give Mom and Dad the option to follow me."

Jenn sighed. "Okay, then, what's your plan?"

"Well, I don't want to say too much, but I wondered if you guys could get in touch with Ron and Taylor for a visit?"

I'd thought about it for a while, and their good family friends were nearby and would likely be receptive to hosting me for a bit while I got some distance from my family and figured out what to do next.

"Of course. Anything else?" Jenn asked.

"Umm, not right now. Will you just let me know when you've gotten ahold of them?"

"Sure thing!"

Having that one conversation alone made me feel better.

A FEW DAYS PASSED, and Adam and Jenn unexpectedly showed up all the way from Oregon. I was so shocked when I saw them I didn't even run to greet them like I normally would. I was sure they were there to give away my plan.

My heart beat heavily in my chest, and I could feel it all over my body.

Mom and Dad were very surprised to see them.

"What are you guys doing way out here?" Mom asked.

"We thought a surprise visit with the family would be a nice change of pace. Plus, it's so beautiful up here when everything starts to turn green. Don't you think, Jenn?"

My sister smiled and grabbed Adam's hand. "It's really the best."

"Do you know how long you'll be staying?" Dad asked, and I think all of us were wondering the same thing.

"Only a few days, I think. We have to get back to work next week."

I turned to Jenn. "If you have time, we should take a walk around the area, and I can show you some of the cool stuff I've found since we got here."

"Sure! Adam and I would love that," my sister agreed.

"Great! We'll get something together for dinner while you're on your walk," Mom said.

I was grateful they hadn't tried to hold us back.

Jenn and Adam were right. This area really was beautiful in the spring. The new growth was so lush and green as we walked, and the early flowers were sprouting all over the place. Even the smell of the fresh grass and brush added to my hopes for the change soon to come in my life.

When we were far enough away from camp, Jenn finally spoke up. "Okay, Sapph, fill us in on the rest of this plan of yours. Adam and I couldn't sit back and watch you do this on your own, so we had to come up and make sure you got where you needed to go, at the very least."

I smiled at them. It was kind of them to want to help me like they did, but they did not have to come all the way from Oregon in order to do it. But since they were here, no sense in keeping them out of the loop. "Well, I gave Ron and Taylor a call and asked them if it was okay if I stayed with them for a little while until I could get myself together enough to move on. They agreed. I figured it would be better to go with them because it'd be a while before Mom and Dad caught on to where I was, and it would give me a chance to build up enough confidence to make sure I never went back if they came for me."

"That makes sense. So, how are you gonna get there?" Adam asked.

"My plan was to go the long way. I'm going to cross the river in the canoe and hike my way to the safe house. It'll throw off the trail more than going the short way, I think."

"How were you going to get the canoe back to camp?"

I swallowed. "I wasn't going to take it back. If it went missing, it went missing. That was it."

Jenn and Adam exchanged a look before turning to me.

"We want to help you," Jenn said.

I blinked at them. "You don't have to do that—"

"We don't have to, but we want to. The whole reason we came here was to help you. You can't stop us now. You might as well involve us."

I paused and thought about it. *It would be easier if I didn't have to hike.*

"Fine," I agreed.

We spent the rest of the walk revising my plan.

When I said I wanted to start soon, they suggested we begin tonight.

"The sooner, the better," Adam explained, and I agreed with him. I'd been wanting to leave my parents since before we left the cabin.

I couldn't believe how fast it was all happening, but I was grateful to have some loved ones to help me out now.

WAITING for everyone to fall asleep was torture. The longest hours of my life were spent staring at the dark ceiling of my tent. I checked the watch Adam had given me for the thousandth time, and the bright green numbers told me it was ten o'clock.

I listened to see if I could hear anyone rustling around having a hard time sleeping. When I was met with silence, I picked up my small bag of clothes and carefully unzipped my tent to leave.

The nice thing about Mom and Dad sleeping in a camper was that it was far less likely they'd end up seeing or hearing me head out. So, besides making sure I stayed quiet as I went, I knew I was basically free to go.

Per the plan, I walked a mile and a half down the way to the boat launch. Jenn and Adam brought a canoe in from the other side and had it pulled up on shore waiting for me.

I sighed and rushed to hug both of them.

"Thank you!" I sniffed. I was so grateful they were

on my side right then. It would have taken me so much longer to do everything alone.

They both smiled at me, and Adam ruffled my hair before he and Jenn got the canoe ready and we were in the water.

I looked back the way I'd come to be sure no one was following me. To be honest, I wasn't really sure what would happen if I got caught, but I knew Dad well enough that he would likely punish me for trying to run away.

Still, there was no one coming through the trees searching for me. I was safe.

The soft sloshing of the paddles moving through the water was all that could be heard as we made our way across the river. I knew if we could make it all the way across the river without anyone seeing us, I was in the clear and would have the head start I needed to get away from my old life.

It was weird to think about it like that, but I guessed that thinking about it with distance now would make it easier to get over later.

Even though it seemed like ages before we reached the other side, it only took us about fifteen minutes. When we made it to shore, we jumped out and pulled the canoe up onto the bank.

The sound of the bottom scraping against the ground echoed across the water, and the three of us froze with wide eyes as soon as we realized how loud it was. I looked out across the river to see if there was any indication of anyone moving around over there, but it was so dark and the night was so quiet, I didn't notice anything unusual.

Heaving a sigh at the all-clear, we rushed up the bank to where their truck was parked. I knew this might be where we'd be discovered since the truck engine was so loud, but I had to count on our head start.

We jumped in, with me sitting between my sister and her husband. Adam turned the ignition, and the truck came to life like a jet engine taking off. I felt the rumbling beneath me, and my heart was racing faster than I'd ever experienced before.

He backed up and then gunned it out of the long drive that would take us to the main road. I looked behind us periodically to be sure we weren't being followed, but still, everything was dark, and the world was quiet.

"Sapph, it's okay. You're safe now," Jenn reassured me, as she put her arms around me in a hug.

I blinked at her. She had the kindest face, and took such good care of me, I couldn't keep it together anymore. I cried. I felt the weight of everything I had done collapse on me. And Jenn held me while I fell apart.

Thinking about the risks they'd taken to help me made me sob even more. I felt terrible for putting them in that position, but I knew, now, I couldn't have done it without them.

My emotional exhaustion had me out like a light in no time. I didn't even notice until the truck jostled me awake and I realized we were parked.

Standing in the headlights on the front porch of a small log cabin stood a hippie-looking couple who were smiling at the truck and our arrival. Ron and Taylor were young and lived on the edge of the woods. They loved the wilderness and artsy things and decided this secluded place in the middle of Canada was the perfect place to settle down.

Even though Ron and Taylor were my brother-in-law's friends more than anyone else's, they knew the rest of my family well.

What was really just eight miles away from my parents' camp, was a really long way around from the other side of the river. We decided it was safer if we threw off the scent and came in from a different direction.

"You're sure you don't wanna come back with us, Sapphire?" Adam asked before turning off the engine.

I nodded, "Yeah. I mean, I appreciate everything you've done, but if I went back with you, Mom and Dad would instantly know where I was and would come and get me. I can't do that to you."

He pursed his lips, but agreed.

I'd reached out to Ron and Taylor to stay with them a short while because I knew it would take Mom and Dad time to figure out where I'd run off to. It was an obvious place right under my parents' noses, and after hearing my story, Ron and Taylor had been more than willing to let me stay as long as I needed to before getting back on my feet.

Really, I just wanted to gain enough strength to face Mom and Dad when they eventually came for me.

I climbed out of the truck and turned to face Jenn. "Thank you for coming all the way here and helping me."

"Family will always be there to support you, Sapph. Even if it's not the family you think. Adam and I are always here for you."

I rushed in to hug her again. "I love you," I mumbled into her shirt.

"We love you, too, kid. Now, get a move on. It's getting late," Adam said, coming in and hugging the two of us together.

I pulled back. "When Mom calls you, please tell them you don't know where I am, okay?"

"Of course. We'll see you soon, okay?" Jenn waved as they climbed back into their truck to leave.

I nodded and turned toward the cottage when they pulled out and headed back to where they were staying.

Ron and Taylor were still waiting on the porch and waved me over when I was finished saying goodbye.

Taylor grabbed me when I got close enough and wrapped me up in a tight embrace. "Everything's gonna be okay, you know?"

I nodded. Despite everything being so new and scary and uncertain, I knew deep down it would be. Not only because all of these people who cared about me said so, but because I could feel it, too.

They led me into their tiny cottage and took me to a hidden loft above their pantry with a bed, where I could settle in and stay. The home felt so safe and warm. I hadn't even realized how cold it still was in these spring months during the night.

The loft was secluded. It felt like an appropriate hiding place considering.

The three of us said goodnight before I truly relaxed and fell fast asleep.

OVER THE NEXT SEVERAL DAYS, I spent my time feeling antsy and pacing around the tiny cabin. They didn't say anything, but I'm sure my agitated movements drove Ron and Taylor nuts.

Thankfully, they were patient with me as I made the adjustments I needed to. They encouraged me to step outside and take walks in the woods. They were good at simply being, which was something I probably could have worked on.

Under different circumstances, I would have loved to explore the new woods around their home. But I was afraid of being discovered. I didn't want any passersby to see me and word to get back to Mom and Dad about where I was.

I didn't want them to arrive any quicker than they needed to.

The day I was dreading arrived sooner than I was ready for.

I was laying in my bed in the loft, counting the knots in the wooden ceiling, when a knock sounded at the door.

We hadn't had any visitors since I arrived, so I knew it was for me.

I listened and heard two different female voices

before footsteps padded through the house and into the kitchen below.

"Sapphire?" Taylor called.

I sighed before sitting up and looking over the edge at her. I hoped my expression was pleading enough that she would go back and tell Mom I didn't want to see her or that I wasn't there.

"Your mom is here, and she wants to speak with you," she told me gently. Her tone of voice was reassuring, and I heaved a sigh as she waved me down.

There was no avoiding it.

My nerves fired, and I felt jittery and shaky as I climbed down the ladder to follow her to the door. There was this weird numbness in my brain I couldn't think out of.

Taylor noticed me struggling and put her hand on my upper back to encourage and reassure me that she was there for me and that I could face this.

As I walked into the front room, Mom was standing in the front entry. I slowly walked up and stopped just out of reach.

It was weird. She was right there, close enough I could have leaped into her arms, but she had this expression on her face that looked angry and sad and lost all at the same time.

I didn't know what any of it meant or what she was going to do, so I stood back and waited. It was painful to do so, but I did all the same.

She took a breath before speaking, "Get your things, Sapphire. We're leaving."

I continued staring at her for a moment. I felt my

heart jump when she said that, but I didn't react to her. I didn't even move.

Taylor's hand was still on my back, steady and warm and there for me.

"Right. Now!" Mom said in a firm voice she rarely ever used with me. I guessed when I didn't respond she was trying to take matters into her own hands.

While I had no preconceived notions of how this day would go when Mom finally did show up at the door, I was shocked at how she behaved. I expected her to be sad that I left and beg me to come back. Even an apology would have been something! Just a small feeling of being valued by the one person I loved the most in the whole world, but that wasn't what was happening.

"No," I said. It was soft but firm. She needed to know everything that she and Dad had allowed to happen was inexcusable and that I would not put up with it anymore.

I was prepared for her to smack me for talking back, or grab me and force me to leave with her.

Instead, she looked at me with a blank expression, shrugged her shoulders, and turned back to the Ford.

I stared, searching for some sort of sign that she had to be joking. That she'd turn around and cry and plead with me again. But she didn't. She got into the truck and left.

What had already been my cracked and fragile heart shattered at that very moment.

Being a steady presence during the encounter, Taylor allowed me to turn and run back to the loft, where I sobbed harder than I ever had before. I had never felt more abandoned in my life, and even though I was the one that left in the first place, I expected some amount of care and concern to come to me and show me things would be different and that I was wanted.

But Mom's actions proved that I didn't mean that much to them.

I don't know how long I cried, but I woke up with my hair and face drenched in snot and tears. The loft really was safe. I'd let go of a lot there.

I laid in my bed and thought about what happened with that visit from Mom. While I still felt broken and lost, some pieces were starting to fit into place and make sense.

If anything, I could appreciate there wasn't anything tying me to them anymore. I survived, just like I promised, and I had been freed because of it.

ACKNOWLEDGMENTS

First, I would like to send all my love and appreciation to my family and friends who supported me on this journey. I know it can be hard watching things from the sidelines sometimes, but your patience and help as we've worked through this process has been beyond wonderful.

I'd also like to give a big thank you to Chris Cannon (Photography) for having just the right photo to represent my story! I am forever grateful to have been able to connect with you. And to Lois Budesheim, our editor, for being willing to take on my story and making it the best version it could be.

Here's to all of our pre-launch readers, as well. All of your feedback and advice went into every detail down to just days before Survive was set to launch, and for that, I am eternally grateful for your help. I'd especially like to give a shoutout to Don Bisdorf for all of your final recommendations on the manuscript, and Kim

Hampton for being so invested in my story so early on. It wouldn't be what it is without you.

And to Lexi Mohney, an incredible coach, mentor, ghostwriter, and friend who never gave up on me. Who believed in this story and let me process this journey at my own pace, which made it exactly what it needed to be. I will forever be thankful to you and blessed you came into my life. Thank you.

Finally, to Clementine Willowilde for helping create the book cover that will forever go before the story! I am so thankful for your creative abilities and I'm so blessed you came onto this project when you did.

## ABOUT THE AUTHOR

Sapphire Geer is a freelance financial advisor based in the Pacific Northwest. She lives with her husband and puppy, and she loves being home as her work takes her on the road a lot.

She has three sons, whom she adores. She loves receiving silly jokes and messages from them out of the blue and is always looking forward to the next holiday where she gets to visit with them again.

Sapphire is a huge advocate for personal well being. She hopes that her new authorship will give her more time and freedom to connect with others and allow her the time to let everyone know that life can actually work for you. She would love to see more people share their stories and flourish from terrible experiences, just like she did when she left the Yukon wilderness.

Made in the USA
Las Vegas, NV
16 November 2020

11005142R00109